MRCPSYCH

PART 1

MCQ PRACTICE PAPERS

PASTEST
Dedicated to your success

MRCPSYCH

PART 1

MCQ PRACTICE PAPERS

Gin S Malhi MB ChB BSc(Hons) MRCPsych
Clinical Lecturer, Social Genetic and Developmental
Research Centre, Institute of Psychiatry,
University of London

Manny S Bagary BSc(Hons) MBBS MRCPsych
Clinical Research Fellow, Department of Neuropsychiatry,
Institute of Neurology, Queen Square, London

Sukhi S Shergill BSc(Hons) MBBS MRCPsych
Wellcome Clinical Fellow, Department of Psychological
Medicine, Institute of Psychiatry,
University of London

© 2000 PASTEST
Egerton Court
Parkgate Estate
Knutsford
Cheshire WA16 8DX

Telephone: 01565 752000

First edition 2000

ISBN 1 901198 12 X

A catalogue record for this book is available from the British Library.

Typeset by Breeze Ltd, Manchester.
Printed by MFP Design and Print, Stretford, Manchester

CONTENTS

PREFACE

The MRCPsych examination is administered by the Royal College of Psychiatrists twice a year and consists of two parts. This book is written for the Part 1 Multiple Choice Question Examination Paper which is the only written component of Part 1.

The Multiple Choice Question Paper has to be passed in order to be able to sit the clinical component of the examination. The paper covers both clinical and basic science topics and places particular emphasis on psychopathology and psychology. It consists of 50 questions each of which is composed of a 'stem' and five related items. The responses are indicated as true or false and there is no longer a penalty for answering incorrectly. Therefore all the questions and related items should be attempted. The time allowed for completion of the paper is ninety minutes.

Preparation for the examination should begin in good time and most candidates require a period of four to six months. It is important from the outset to be equipped with the appropriate texts and have a clear idea of the format of the examination and the extent of knowledge required. It is therefore best to obtain the latest guidelines in place at the time of application from the Royal College. The books that we recommend are listed on page 119.

Revision should be tailored to the examination and a set time should be ideally set aside on a daily basis. Questions can be used to revise new learning and test knowledge but it is essential at some point to attempt a complete paper under examination conditions.

The MRCPsych examination is designed to differentiate between candidates and so it is predictably difficult. However, it is important to remember that exam success is achievable and that the likelihood of this is significantly increased by thorough preparation.

Even with the best preparation there is bound to be some anxiety both immediately prior to the examination and on the day itself. Ideally, this should be used to focus learning and enhance performance but this too requires practice and again sitting papers under examination conditions should help.

This book has been written with these considerations in mind and it is hoped that it will be of help to those sitting the Part 1 MRCPsych Examination.

G S Mahli
M S Bagary
S S Shergill

MCQ ANSWER SHEET

The Royal College of Psychiatrists

ANSWER SHEET

Name

Instructions
- This form will be read by a machine
- Please use an HB pencil. Rub out all errors thoroughly
- Fill lozenges with a single line e.g. cT⸱ ⊨
- Do **NOT** use ticks, crosses or circles
- T = True F = False
- Fill in the relevant Examination lozenge

Important Notes
Erasures should be left clean, with no smudges where possible (the document reading machine will accept the darkest response for each item)

CANDIDATE NUMBER

c0⸱	c0⸱	c0⸱	c0⸱	c0⸱
c1⸱	c1⸱	c1⸱	c1⸱	c1⸱
c2⸱	c2⸱	c2⸱	c2⸱	c2⸱
c3⸱	c3⸱	c3⸱	c3⸱	c3⸱
c4⸱	c4⸱	c4⸱	c4⸱	c4⸱
c5⸱	c5⸱	c5⸱	c5⸱	c5⸱
c6⸱	c6⸱	c6⸱	c6⸱	c6⸱
c7⸱	c7⸱	c7⸱	c7⸱	c7⸱
c8⸱	c8⸱	c8⸱	c8⸱	c8⸱
c9⸱	c9⸱	c9⸱	c9⸱	c9⸱

EXAMINATION

Part I	c ⸱
Part II Basic Sciences	c ⸱
Part II Clinical Studies	c ⸱

	a	b	c	d	e
1	cT⸱ cF⸱	cT⸱ cF⸱	cT⸱ cF⸱	cT⸱ cF⸱	cT⸱ cF⸱
2	cT⸱ cF⸱	cT⸱ cF⸱	cT⸱ cF⸱	cT⸱ cF⸱	cT⸱ cF⸱
3	cT⸱ cF⸱	cT⸱ cF⸱	cT⸱ cF⸱	cT⸱ cF⸱	cT⸱ cF⸱
4	cT⸱ cF⸱	cT⸱ cF⸱	cT⸱ cF⸱	cT⸱ cF⸱	cT⸱ cF⸱
5	cT⸱ cF⸱	cT⸱ cF⸱	cT⸱ cF⸱	cT⸱ cF⸱	cT⸱ cF⸱

	a	b	c	d	e
6	cT⸱ cF⸱	cT⸱ cF⸱	cT⸱ cF⸱	cT⸱ cF⸱	cT⸱ cF⸱
7	cT⸱ cF⸱	cT⸱ cF⸱	cT⸱ cF⸱	cT⸱ cF⸱	cT⸱ cF⸱
8	cT⸱ cF⸱	cT⸱ cF⸱	cT⸱ cF⸱	cT⸱ cF⸱	cT⸱ cF⸱
9	cT⸱ cF⸱	cT⸱ cF⸱	cT⸱ cF⸱	cT⸱ cF⸱	cT⸱ cF⸱
10	cT⸱ cF⸱	cT⸱ cF⸱	cT⸱ cF⸱	cT⸱ cF⸱	cT⸱ cF⸱

	a	b	c	d	e
11	cT⸱ cF⸱	cT⸱ cF⸱	cT⸱ cF⸱	cT⸱ cF⸱	cT⸱ cF⸱
12	cT⸱ cF⸱	cT⸱ cF⸱	cT⸱ cF⸱	cT⸱ cF⸱	cT⸱ cF⸱
13	cT⸱ cF⸱	cT⸱ cF⸱	cT⸱ cF⸱	cT⸱ cF⸱	cT⸱ cF⸱
14	cT⸱ cF⸱	cT⸱ cF⸱	cT⸱ cF⸱	cT⸱ cF⸱	cT⸱ cF⸱
15	cT⸱ cF⸱	cT⸱ cF⸱	cT⸱ cF⸱	cT⸱ cF⸱	cT⸱ cF⸱

	a	b	c	d	e
16	cT⸱ cF⸱	cT⸱ cF⸱	cT⸱ cF⸱	cT⸱ cF⸱	cT⸱ cF⸱
17	cT⸱ cF⸱	cT⸱ cF⸱	cT⸱ cF⸱	cT⸱ cF⸱	cT⸱ cF⸱
18	cT⸱ cF⸱	cT⸱ cF⸱	cT⸱ cF⸱	cT⸱ cF⸱	cT⸱ cF⸱
19	cT⸱ cF⸱	cT⸱ cF⸱	cT⸱ cF⸱	cT⸱ cF⸱	cT⸱ cF⸱
20	cT⸱ cF⸱	cT⸱ cF⸱	cT⸱ cF⸱	cT⸱ cF⸱	cT⸱ cF⸱

	a	b	c	d	e
21	cT⸱ cF⸱	cT⸱ cF⸱	cT⸱ cF⸱	cT⸱ cF⸱	cT⸱ cF⸱
22	cT⸱ cF⸱	cT⸱ cF⸱	cT⸱ cF⸱	cT⸱ cF⸱	cT⸱ cF⸱
23	cT⸱ cF⸱	cT⸱ cF⸱	cT⸱ cF⸱	cT⸱ cF⸱	cT⸱ cF⸱
24	cT⸱ cF⸱	cT⸱ cF⸱	cT⸱ cF⸱	cT⸱ cF⸱	cT⸱ cF⸱
25	cT⸱ cF⸱	cT⸱ cF⸱	cT⸱ cF⸱	cT⸱ cF⸱	cT⸱ cF⸱

	a	b	c	d	e
26	cT⸱ cF⸱	cT⸱ cF⸱	cT⸱ cF⸱	cT⸱ cF⸱	cT⸱ cF⸱
27	cT⸱ cF⸱	cT⸱ cF⸱	cT⸱ cF⸱	cT⸱ cF⸱	cT⸱ cF⸱
28	cT⸱ cF⸱	cT⸱ cF⸱	cT⸱ cF⸱	cT⸱ cF⸱	cT⸱ cF⸱
29	cT⸱ cF⸱	cT⸱ cF⸱	cT⸱ cF⸱	cT⸱ cF⸱	cT⸱ cF⸱
30	cT⸱ cF⸱	cT⸱ cF⸱	cT⸱ cF⸱	cT⸱ cF⸱	cT⸱ cF⸱

	a	b	c	d	e
31	cT⸱ cF⸱	cT⸱ cF⸱	cT⸱ cF⸱	cT⸱ cF⸱	cT⸱ cF⸱
32	cT⸱ cF⸱	cT⸱ cF⸱	cT⸱ cF⸱	cT⸱ cF⸱	cT⸱ cF⸱
33	cT⸱ cF⸱	cT⸱ cF⸱	cT⸱ cF⸱	cT⸱ cF⸱	cT⸱ cF⸱
34	cT⸱ cF⸱	cT⸱ cF⸱	cT⸱ cF⸱	cT⸱ cF⸱	cT⸱ cF⸱
35	cT⸱ cF⸱	cT⸱ cF⸱	cT⸱ cF⸱	cT⸱ cF⸱	cT⸱ cF⸱

	a	b	c	d	e
36	cT⸱ cF⸱	cT⸱ cF⸱	cT⸱ cF⸱	cT⸱ cF⸱	cT⸱ cF⸱
37	cT⸱ cF⸱	cT⸱ cF⸱	cT⸱ cF⸱	cT⸱ cF⸱	cT⸱ cF⸱
38	cT⸱ cF⸱	cT⸱ cF⸱	cT⸱ cF⸱	cT⸱ cF⸱	cT⸱ cF⸱
39	cT⸱ cF⸱	cT⸱ cF⸱	cT⸱ cF⸱	cT⸱ cF⸱	cT⸱ cF⸱
40	cT⸱ cF⸱	cT⸱ cF⸱	cT⸱ cF⸱	cT⸱ cF⸱	cT⸱ cF⸱

	a	b	c	d	e
41	cT⸱ cF⸱	cT⸱ cF⸱	cT⸱ cF⸱	cT⸱ cF⸱	cT⸱ cF⸱
42	cT⸱ cF⸱	cT⸱ cF⸱	cT⸱ cF⸱	cT⸱ cF⸱	cT⸱ cF⸱
43	cT⸱ cF⸱	cT⸱ cF⸱	cT⸱ cF⸱	cT⸱ cF⸱	cT⸱ cF⸱
44	cT⸱ cF⸱	cT⸱ cF⸱	cT⸱ cF⸱	cT⸱ cF⸱	cT⸱ cF⸱
45	cT⸱ cF⸱	cT⸱ cF⸱	cT⸱ cF⸱	cT⸱ cF⸱	cT⸱ cF⸱

	a	b	c	d	e
46	cT⸱ cF⸱	cT⸱ cF⸱	cT⸱ cF⸱	cT⸱ cF⸱	cT⸱ cF⸱
47	cT⸱ cF⸱	cT⸱ cF⸱	cT⸱ cF⸱	cT⸱ cF⸱	cT⸱ cF⸱
48	cT⸱ cF⸱	cT⸱ cF⸱	cT⸱ cF⸱	cT⸱ cF⸱	cT⸱ cF⸱
49	cT⸱ cF⸱	cT⸱ cF⸱	cT⸱ cF⸱	cT⸱ cF⸱	cT⸱ cF⸱
50	cT⸱ cF⸱	cT⸱ cF⸱	cT⸱ cF⸱	cT⸱ cF⸱	cT⸱ cF⸱

Speedwell Computing Services Tel (01604) 410041

Sample answer sheet reproduced by kind permission of the Royal College of Psychiatrists

MULTIPLE CHOICE QUESTION PAPER 1

50 questions: time allowed 1 hour 30 minutes

1.1 **Nomothetic theories of personality include**

- ☐ A Eysenck's type theory
- ☐ B Catell's trait theory
- ☐ C Allport's trait theory
- ☐ D Maslow's hierarchy of needs
- ☐ E Kelly's personal construct theory

1.2 **Imipramine**

- ☐ A is a tertiary amine
- ☐ B does not have anticholinergic side-effects
- ☐ C has a quinidine-like effect on premature ventricular contractions
- ☐ D is effective in the treatment of panic disorder
- ☐ E has no effect on serotonin re-uptake

1.3 **According to Klein, psychotic defence mechanisms include**

- ☐ A splitting
- ☐ B repression
- ☐ C displacement
- ☐ D projection
- ☐ E denial

1.4 **With regard to homoeostasis**

- ☐ A the term was coined by Lang
- ☐ B homoeostatic drive theory is by Canon
- ☐ C the ventro-medial hypothalamus is a satiety centre
- ☐ D the lateral hypothalamus is a thirst centre
- ☐ E the lateral hypothalamus stimulates hunger

1.5   **With regard to bystander intervention**

- ☐ A   impulsive helping is more likely in an emergency
- ☐ B   females are more empathic than males
- ☐ C   males are more likely to intervene than females
- ☐ D   agentic helping is more common in males
- ☐ E   personality differences have been consistently reported in studies of bystander intervention

1.6   **In language development, the following variables are considered important in children who are exposed to language:**

- ☐ A   developmental maturation
- ☐ B   cognition
- ☐ C   geographical location
- ☐ D   culture
- ☐ E   training

1.7   **The following can be demonstrated in a newborn:**

- ☐ A   pupillary light reflex
- ☐ B   optokinetic reflex
- ☐ C   saccadic eye movements
- ☐ D   accommodation
- ☐ E   20:20 visual acuity

1.8   **The important determinants of maternal behaviour in humans include**

- ☐ A   oestrogen
- ☐ B   progesterone
- ☐ C   oxytocin
- ☐ D   early experiences of the mother
- ☐ E   characteristics of the neonate

1.9   Neologisms

□   A   are new words or familiar words used in novel way
□   B   are found within schizophasia
□   C   occur in those with schizophrenia
□   D   occur in those with Gilles de la Tourette syndrome
□   E   occur in those with Wernicke's aphasia

1.10   Melanie Klein conceptualised infant development using the following terms:

□   A   anal phase
□   B   latency
□   C   pubertal
□   D   good and bad objects
□   E   depressive position

1.11   Antisocial personality disorder is generally considered to include the following characteristics:

□   A   lack of feelings for others
□   B   behaviour not modified by experience
□   C   sensitivity to humiliation and rebuff
□   D   emotional coldness
□   E   attention to detail

1.12   Verbigeration

□   A   is seen in schizophrenia
□   B   means literally 'talking point'
□   C   is also referred to as word salad
□   D   is a form of stereotype
□   E   is a persistent response to a prior stimulus

1.13 Concomitant administration of the following drugs will cause elevation in the blood levels of tricyclic antidepressants:

□ A phenytoin
□ B chlorpromazine
□ C haloperidol
□ D phenelzine
□ E lithium

1.14 Corticotrophin releasing hormone (CRH)

□ A is found in cerebral cortex
□ B increases sexual behaviour
□ C increases blood pressure and heart rate
□ D increases feeding
□ E increases plasma glucose levels

1.15 With regard to Maslow's hierarchy of needs

□ A it is a humanistic theory
□ B it is not hierarchical
□ C high level needs create later evolutionary developments
□ D self-actualisation is linked to the biological character of needs
□ E only particular individuals are capable of self-actualising

1.16 Recognised combinations of antidepressant medications include

□ A clomipramine and thyroxine
□ B fluoxetine and lithium
□ C clomipramine and lithium and tryptophan
□ D tranylcypromine and clomipramine
□ E sertraline and pindolol

1.17   Concerning clozapine

- ☐ A   it causes sialorrhoea
- ☐ B   the risk of agranulocytosis in the UK is less than 1%
- ☐ C   weight gain plateaus at six months
- ☐ D   neuroleptic malignant syndrome has been reported
- ☐ E   it is an atypical neuroleptic

1.18   Circular reaction processes described in Piaget's model of cognitive development include

- ☐ A   reaction formation
- ☐ B   accommodation
- ☐ C   rejection
- ☐ D   assimilation
- ☐ E   attachment

1.19   Argyll Robertson pupil is characterised by

- ☐ A   arcus senilis
- ☐ B   large size
- ☐ C   loss of light reaction
- ☐ D   contraction with accommodation
- ☐ E   an irregular outline

1.20   The following statements are true of the EEG:

- ☐ A   alpha rhythm arises posteriorly
- ☐ B   the flat trace is diagnostic of brain death
- ☐ C   beta activity has high frequency and high amplitude
- ☐ D   lambda waves are pathological
- ☐ E   mu activity is abolished by movement of the contralateral limb

1.21   The parasympathetic nervous system mediates

☐ A   peristalsis
☐ B   salivary secretion
☐ C   micturition
☐ D   sweating
☐ E   tachycardia

1.22   Catecholamines

☐ A   include acetylcholine
☐ B   are synthesised from phenylalanine
☐ C   include serotonin
☐ D   are monoamines
☐ E   are false neurotransmitters

1.23   During pregnancy

☐ A   lithium causes increased risk of Ebstein abnormality in the
          second trimester
☐ B   lithium should be discontinued throughout
☐ C   carbamazepine is a useful alternative to lithium during
          pregnancy
☐ D   benzodiazepines cause an increased risk of cleft palate in the
          first trimester
☐ E   ECT is contraindicated in the first trimester

**1.24   The following figures are correctly associated with the
          corresponding term:**

☐ A   Kahlbaum   demence precoce
☐ B   Heckler   hebephrenia
☐ C   Griesinger   Einheitpsychose
☐ D   Schneider   dementia praecox
☐ E   Jaspers   catatonia

1.25   In Crow's type I schizophrenia

☐ A   the cerebral ventricles are dilated
☐ B   the onset of symptoms is acute
☐ C   cognition is normal
☐ D   response to treatment is poor
☐ E   there is a positive family history

1.26   In the aetiology of schizophrenia excessive amounts of the following substances have been implicated:

☐ A   serotonin
☐ B   dopamine
☐ C   glutamate
☐ D   dimethyl-tryptamine
☐ E   aspartate

1.27   The following types of schizophrenia are correctly described:

☐ A   simple; simply has one set of positive psychotic symptoms such as hallucinations
☐ B   catatonic; predominantly motor abnormalities
☐ C   residual; thought disorder and disturbance of affect
☐ D   hebephrenic; marked by apathy and emotional blunting
☐ E   paranoid; delusions and hallucinations with relatively well preserved personality

1.28   In schizophrenia factors associated with a favourable outcome include

☐ A   being married
☐ B   normal neuropsychological profile
☐ C   previous episodes of psychosis
☐ D   male gender
☐ E   impaired pre-morbid personality

1.29   Recognised features of depression include

☐ A   irritability
☐ B   guilt
☐ C   suicidal ideation
☐ D   nihilistic delusions
☐ E   erotic delusions

1.30   Depression is associated with

☐ A   decreased monocyte activity
☐ B   increased interleukin-2 activity
☐ C   decreased natural killer cells
☐ D   increased T-cell replication
☐ E   raised ESR

1.31   In bipolar patients

☐ A   females often experience their first episode after childbirth
☐ B   manic relapses are more likely in the summer
☐ C   there is an activating response to L-dopa
☐ D   early onset conveys a better prognosis
☐ E   life events may precipitate relapse

1.32   The following statements are true of suicide:

☐ A   a family history of suicide increases the risk
☐ B   deliberate self-poisoning is more common in young females
       compared with elderly females
☐ C   hanging is the most frequent method in males
☐ D   seasonal variation is more marked in females
☐ E   in Post-Traumatic Stress Disorder (PTSD) combat related guilt
       increases risk

1.33   Agoraphobia is commonly associated with

☐   A   fear of tunnels
☐   B   equal prevalence in males and females
☐   C   obsessional symptoms
☐   D   lower social class
☐   E   onset in childhood

1.34   Depressive illness

☐   A   carries a lifetime risk of 20%
☐   B   has a point prevalence between 4–7%
☐   C   is more common in females
☐   D   may be precipitated by disorders of cortisol
☐   E   may be precipitated by disorders of thyroxine

1.35   When schizophrenic patients are compared with controls

☐   A   they have smaller ventricles on MRI
☐   B   they have an increased incidence of obstetric complications in their birth records
☐   C   they show no structural changes in medial temporal lobe structures
☐   D   neurological soft signs are found in up to 15% of patients, with no specific abnormality
☐   E   smooth pursuit eye movements are abnormal in a proportion of patients

1.36   Alcohol abuse is associated with

☐   A   tuberculosis
☐   B   hepatic fatty infiltration
☐   C   coronary artery disease
☐   D   pancreatitis
☐   E   palmar erythema

1.37 Recognised features of heroin withdrawal include

☐ A rhinorrhoea
☐ B abdominal cramps
☐ C drowsiness
☐ D constipation
☐ E mydriasis

1.38 Characteristic features of Gerstmann's syndrome include

☐ A dyscalculia
☐ B perseveration
☐ C retrograde amnesia
☐ D hyperreflexia
☐ E dystonia

1.39 The following features are associated with Huntington's disease:

☐ A the implicated abnormal gene is on chromosome 4
☐ B there is a reduction of GABA
☐ C death usually occurs within 10 years of onset of symptoms
☐ D there is increased size of the caudate nucleus
☐ E there is increased amplitude of the EEG

1.40 The following statements regarding patients having alcohol dependence are true:

☐ A nearly 50% of patients have another psychiatric diagnosis
☐ B the odds ratio is 21 for a co-morbid diagnosis of antisocial personality disorder
☐ C mania is a more common co-morbid diagnosis than schizophrenia
☐ D the male to female ratio is 8:1
☐ E there is a greater prevalence in middle social classes

1.41 Narcolepsy

☐ A is characterised by cataplexy, sleep paralysis and hypnagogic hallucinations
☐ B is associated with lengthened REM latency
☐ C is identical in presentation to the Kleine–Levin syndrome
☐ D has an association with HLA-DR2
☐ E responds to treatment with amphetamines

1.42 Characteristic features of infantile autism include

☐ A echolalia
☐ B pronominal reversal
☐ C poor comprehension of speech
☐ D compulsive phenomena
☐ E lack of attachment behaviour

1.43 Recognised treatments of enuresis include the following:

☐ A mirtazapine
☐ B amitriptyline
☐ C bell and pad method
☐ D use of a star chart
☐ E imipramine

1.44 Head banging in children is associated with

☐ A frustration
☐ B Lesch–Nyhan syndrome
☐ C blindness
☐ D mental retardation
☐ E neglect

1.45   In anorexia nervosa recognised skin changes include

☐   A   lanugo hair
☐   B   purpura
☐   C   erythema nodosum
☐   D   carotinoderma
☐   E   seborrhoea

1.46   Recognised features of Kleine–Levin syndrome include

☐   A   onset usually in 5th and 6th decades of life
☐   B   anhedonia and reduced libido
☐   C   delusions
☐   D   depressed mood
☐   E   diminished appetite

1.47   Nocturnal enuresis is associated with

☐   A   small families
☐   B   low IQ
☐   C   a family history of nocturnal enuresis
☐   D   a poorer prognosis if primary
☐   E   small bladder capacity

1.48   Criteria of anankastic personality disorder as defined by ICD-10 include

☐   A   rigidity and stubbornness
☐   B   unstable and capricious mood
☐   C   excessive pedantry
☐   D   excessive scrupulousness
☐   E   a combative and tenacious sense of personal rights

1.49   Koro

- ☐ A   affects Chinese males
- ☐ B   occurs in the context of sexual guilt
- ☐ C   involves the belief that the penis will retract into the abdomen
- ☐ D   typically results in depressive and suicidal thoughts
- ☐ E   may lead to thoughts of cannibalism

1.50   Chronic fatigue syndrome

- ☐ A   is best treated with strict bed-rest
- ☐ B   is characterised by hypercortisolaemia
- ☐ C   responds well to high-dose clomipramine
- ☐ D   is also called 'shell-shock'
- ☐ E   is characterised by a microcytic hypochromic anaemia

MULTIPLE CHOICE QUESTION PAPER 1 – ANSWERS

1.1   Answers: A B

Nomothetic theories study personality, using factor analysis to interpret questionnaires to identify common factors which can then be used to study similarities and differences between individuals. The idiographic approach attempts to identify individual uniqueness using detailed study of individuals rather than standardised tests.

1.2   Answers: A C D

Imipramine is a tertiary tricyclic antidepressant that has both noradrenergic and serotonergic effects. It causes anticholinergic side-effects, sedation, seizures and orthostatic hypotension.

1.3   Answers: A D E

Other Kleinian psychotic defence mechanisms include projective identification, omnipotence and grandiosity.

1.4   Answers: B C D E

Homoeostasis was coined by Canon.

1.5   Answers: A B C D

Agentic helping refers to heroism and chivalry.

1.6   Answer: A

Assuming children are exposed to language, it is acquired in a predictable sequential manner according to the rate of individual developmental maturation.

1.7   Answers: A B C

At birth focus is fixed at 20 cm from the newborn's face, accommodation begins at two months and is adult-like at six months. At six to twelve months visual acuity is consistent with the adult range.

1.8   Answers: D E

In humans sex hormones are not considered to be important in determining maternal behaviour.

1.9   **Answers: All true**

Neologisms are new words or those with novel use often formed by combining bits of several words. They occur most often in patient's with schizophrenia, but are also described in Wernicke's aphasia, Gilles de la Tourette syndrome and mania. Schizophasia or word salad often includes neologisms.

1.10   **Answers: D E**

Klein suggested that the mother is split into both good and bad objects dependent on whether she is satisfying the child's needs; this is the paranoid-schizoid position. Once the two objects are reintegrated into one person, the depressive position is reached. This is the prototype for working through adult losses and frustrations. Sigmund Freud suggested the following developmental stages: oral, anal, phallic, latency and genital or pubertal.

1.11   **Answers: A B**

This includes disregard for social restrictions; lack of feeling for others; experience, even punishment, doesn't modify behaviour; and a tendency to blame others offering plausible rationalisations for behaviour.

1.12   **Answers: A D**

Verbigeration is the repetition of fragmented phrases in a form of verbal stereotypy. It is most likely to occur in schizophrenia. Vorbeireden means talking past the point. Word salad is also called schizophasia or speech confusion and in this words are jumbled up such that speech is difficult to understand. The persistence of cued speech beyond its relevance is termed perseveration.

1.13   **Answers: B C D**

Barbiturates, phenytoin and rifampicin induce hepatic enzymes resulting in lower tricyclic levels. Phenothiazine (chlorpromazine) and butyrophenone (haloperidol), antipsychotics and MAOIs (phenelzine) inhibit these enzymes with risks of precipitating toxic levels. Lithium does not affect this system.

1.14   **Answers: A C E**

CRH is found in many areas of the brain. It inhibits feeding and sexual behaviour and is probably involved in the aetiology of anorexia nervosa and depression.

1.15   **Answers: A C E**

Everybody is capable of self-actualisation although few achieve this. Self-actualisation is linked to life experience rather than to the biological character of need.

1.16   **Answers: A B C E**

The combination of MAOIs and TCAs is potentially very dangerous as there have been case reports of fatalities.

1.17   **Answers: All true**

Although neuroleptic malignant syndrome has been reported it is rare.

1.18   **Answers: B D**

The circular reaction as described by Piaget involves the shifting of equilibrium upon experiencing something outside of an existing schema. This disequilibrium prompts accommodation and the development of new schemas which are incorporated through assimilation to regain equilibrium.

1.19   **Answers: D E**

The pupil is small, irregular, fixed, does not react to light but contracts with accommodation. Usually due to neuro-syphilitic lesions interrupting fibres from the pre-tectal nucleus to the Edinger-Westphal nucleus of the oculomotor nerve bilaterally. Parasympathetic connections from the Edinger–Westphal nucleus to the constrictor pupillae remain intact hence pupillary constriction with accommodation is maintained.

1.20   **Answers: A E**

The EEG is a recording of the electrical potential activity of the brain and consists of:

Beta	Over 13 Hz	Low amplitude
Alpha	8 to 13 Hz	
Theta	4 to 8 Hz	
Delta	Under 4 Hz	High amplitude

Lambda waves occur in the occipital regions with the eyes closed and are related to ocular movements. Mu waves occur over the motor cortex during motor activity. A flat trace may occur with hypothermia and is thus not diagnostic of brain death.

1.21   **Answers: A B C**

The parasympathetic nervous system has a secreto-motor function and controls gut motility and micturition. Tachycardia and sweating are mediated via the sympathetic nervous system.

1.22   **Answers: B D**

A catecholamine is a catechol nucleus with an amine group attached. They are synthesised from phenylalanine, a precursor of tyrosine and include dopamine, noradrenaline and adrenaline. Monoamines include dopamine, noradrenaline and serotonin.

1.23   **Answer: D**

Lithium causes an increased risk of Ebstein abnormality (tricuspid valve abnormalities) in the first trimester of pregnancy. The decision to discontinue lithium during pregnancy should be based on the risk benefit to each individual patient. Sub-therapeutic levels may occur during pregnancy due to the increased volume of distribution and increased GFR. Toxicity may occur in the puerperium due to the rapid fall in the volume of distribution and GFR. Therefore levels need to be monitored throughout and during pregnancy.

Carbamazepine and valproate are not useful alternatives to lithium during pregnancy due to increased risk of spina bifida.

1.24   **Answers: B C**

Kahlbaum described catatonia. Schneider described first and second rank symptoms of schizophrenia. Jaspers described the non-understandability of schizophrenia-'the praecox feeling'. Dementia praecox was coined by Kraepelin.

1.25   **Answers: B C E**

Type I: predominantly positive symptoms with a good response to treatment. The ventricles are normal, as is cognition, and the patient has a relatively good prognosis.

1.26   **Answers: A B D**

Glutamate and aspartate are excitatory amino acids and it is proposed that these are lacking or that there is a paucity of their receptors.

1.27   **Answers: B E**

Simple schizophrenia characteristically lacks positive psychotic symptoms. There is a gradual deterioration with increasing eccentricity. Hebephrenic schizophrenia features thought disorder and prominent disturbance of affect. Residual schizophrenia is 'the residue' and is marked by apathy, emotional blunting and the eccentricity of a defect state.

1.28   **Answers: A B**

Associated with favourable outcome are: being female (unless treated with clozapine), older age of onset, being married, with normal premorbid personality and no history of psychiatric illness.

1.29   **Answers: A B C D**

Nihilistic delusions are the core feature of Cotard's syndrome which in other aspects does not differ from severe depressive disorder. Erotic delusions are a core feature of De Clérambault's syndrome which is extremely rare and is usually associated with paranoid schizophrenia.

1.30   **Answers: B C D**

The immunological abnormalities in depression are possibly related to hypothallamic-pituitory-adrenal axis dysfunction modulated by type II glucocorticoid receptor.

1.31   **Answers: A B C E**
Early onset conveys a poorer prognosis.

1.32   **Answers: A D E**
Carbon monoxide poisoning is the most frequent method of suicide
in males and deliberate self-poisoning the most frequent in females.
Hanging is the most frequent method in prisons. The incidence of
poisoning and hanging increases with age.

1.33   **Answers: A C**
Agoraphobia is associated with fear of open or confined spaces; fear
of leaving home; fear of places where help is difficult to access. It is
commoner in females (2:1), has normal class distribution and
usually occurs between adolescence and age 35 years. It is
commonly associated with obsessional symptoms, depersonalisation
and depression.

1.34   **Answers: All true**
The point prevalence of major depression varies from 4 to 7%. The
point prevalence of depressive symptoms is 16 to 20%. The lifetime
risk is 20%. There is a female predominance of 2:1. Disorders of
cortisol or thyroxine and iatrogenic causes (steroids, beta-blockers)
can precipitate illness.

1.35   **Answers: B E**
There is an increased incidence of obstetric complication in the
birth records of schizophrenics, supporting the neurodevelopment
hypothesis. CT and MRI scan changes show cerebral atrophy and
enlarged ventricles occur in many patients, regardless of the
duration of illness. Neuropathological studies have shown structural
changes in medial temporal lobe structures due to a atrophy or
dysplasia. Neurological soft signs are common, occurring in up to
60% with no specific abnormalities. Smooth pursuit eye movements
are abnormal as are event related evoked potentials.

1.36 **Answers: All true**

Alcohol abuse is associated with the following: hepatic fatty infiltration, hepatitis and cirrhosis (palmar erythema is associated with liver disease), oesophageal varices, gastritis, pancreatitis and peptic ulceration. Most heavy drinkers also smoke and there is therefore also a strong association with lung cancer. Alcohol abuse is associated with TB, probably because of malnutrition and poor self-hygiene. Moderate drinking is probably a protective factor for coronary artery disease.

1.37 **Answers: A B E**

Features of withdrawal form heroin include: mydriasis, sweating, diarrhoea, rhinorrhoea, abdominal cramps, yawning, nausea, vomiting and lacrimation.

1.38 **Answer: A**

Gerstmann's syndrome, characteristic of a dominant parietal lobe lesion, consists of the following:

- dyscalculia
- dysgraphia
- finger agnosia
- inability to distinguish left from right.

1.39 **Answers: A B**

Huntington's disease begins in the 4th to 5th decade most commonly there is initial clumsiness and twitching of the muscles of the face before the onset of the characteristic choreiform movements. Commonly it is associated with depression in the early stages and subcortical dementia later. There is reduced GABA, unchanged dopamine levels and increased somatostatin. The inheritance is autosomal dominant with complete penetrance; the abnormal gene is on chromosome 4. There is characteristic flattening of the EEG and the caudate nucleus is reduced in size. Death occurs 15–20 years after onset of symptoms.

1.40   **Answers: A B C**

Approximately 50% of patients with alcoholism have another psychiatric diagnosis. The commonest is antisocial personality disorder, odds ratio (OR) 21, other diagnoses are mania (OR 6), schizophrenia (OR 4) and major depression (OR 2). The onset is in the late teens for males, later in females; male to female ratio is 4:1. Rates are highest in lower and upper social classes with increased risk in urban areas, in those who are separated and in those who have ready access to alcohol with lack of restraining social structure (e.g. publicans, entertainers and journalists).

1.41   **Answers: A D E**

Narcolepsy is characterised by episodes of uncontrollable sleep; with one or more of the following: cataplexy (loss of muscle tone), sleep paralysis (transient paralysis with spontaneous recovery) and hypnagogic hallucinations (hallucinations around the period of falling asleep). REM sleep is seen very early from the onset of sleep; this is shortened REM latency. It is associated with HLA-DR2. Treatment is with methylphenidate and amphetamines (although modafinil – a newer non-amphetamine drug is now available). Kleine–Levin syndrome is different from narcolepsy in having episodes of hypersomnia lasting several days, with compulsive eating and auditory/visual hallucinations.

1.42   **Answers: All true**

Abnormalities of language and social interaction are marked and noted early. There is also a liking for routine and consistency. Unusual preoccupation, self-injury and overactivity are also often observed.

1.43   **Answers: B C D E**

The bell and pad method which alerts the child after the bed is wet is probably the most effective method. Tricyclic antidepressants have a high rate of relapse. The use of a star chart is effective in monitoring the problem and is sometimes an effective treatment.

1.44   **Answers: All true**

Head banging usually occurs at night-time from the age of six months. It is usually a means of venting frustration or seeking attention but can also be indicative of severe neglect. More severe self-injury is found in those with mental retardation or Lesch–Nyhan syndrome.

1.45   **Answers: A B D**

The skin is usually dry. There may be bruising, purpura and calluses on the hands.

1.46   **Answers: C D**

This is a disorder of the hypothalamus that is characterised by low mood, hyperphagia, hypersomnia, and hypersexuality. It usually manifests in the second decade of life and is most common in young males.

1.47   **Answers: B C E**

Nocturnal enuresis is the involuntary passage of urine in the absence of physical abnormalities after the age of 5 years. It is associated with low IQ, large families and a positive family history. It is described as primary if present since birth and secondary if it occurs following a dry period of at least six months. The latter has a poorer prognosis.

1.48   **Answers: A C D**

Anankastic personality disorder criteria include feelings of excessive doubt and caution; preoccupation with details; perfectionism that interferes with task completion; undue preoccupation with productivity to the exclusion of pleasure and interpersonal relationships. A combative and tenacious sense of personal rights is a feature of paranoid personality disorder and an unstable and capricious mood is a feature of the impulsive type of emotionally unstable personality disorder.

1.49   **Answers: A B C**

The individual may try to prevent retraction of the penis into the abdomen by tying it up with string.

1.50   **Answers: All false**

Chronic fatigue syndrome usually shows hypocortisolaemia (opposite to that found in major depression) and is best treated with graded exercise. Co-morbid depression is common and this responds to antidepressants. Shell-shock is now described as PTSD. Iron-deficiency anaemia is characteristically microcytic and hypochromic.

50 questions: time allowed 1 hour 30 minutes

2.1   The following are true of personality theories:

☐   A   Eysenck's type theory of personality employs orthogonal factor analysis

☐   B   Cattel's trait theory of personality employs second order factor analysis

☐   C   orthogonal factors are independent of each other

☐   D   oblique factors are independent of each other

☐   E   orthogonal factors are more powerful than oblique factors

2.2   The following are proponents of psychoanalytic theories:

☐   A   Rogers

☐   B   Adler

☐   C   Jung

☐   D   Erikson

☐   E   Kelly

2.3   Q sort

☐   A   is a personality rating

☐   B   rater explicitly compares each trait with other traits between individuals

☐   C   does not rate personal disposition

☐   D   inter rater reliability cannot be assessed

☐   E   test retest reliability cannot be assessed

2.4   In arousal

☐ A   tonic alertness reflects the circadian rhythm
☐ B   phasic alertness reflects temporary variations in arousal in response to novel stimuli
☐ C   the orientating response involves an increase in heart rate
☐ D   the EEG is synchronised during the orientating response
☐ E   habituation occurs in response to repeated presentation of a stimulus

2.5   Sensory memory

☐ A   lasts thirty seconds
☐ B   is modality specific
☐ C   is located in centralised specific cortical areas
☐ D   is disrupted by additional information in the same modality
☐ E   for auditory information is called haptic

2.6   Babbling

☐ A   coincides with a phonetic expansion
☐ B   is secondary to developmental maturation
☐ C   is dependent upon learning
☐ D   occurs in deaf babies
☐ E   occurs in children born to deaf/mute parents

2.7   The following gender differences have been demonstrated:

☐ A   males are more aggressive than females
☐ B   adolescent females have greater verbal ability than adolescent males
☐ C   pre-adolescent males have greater visio-spatial ability than pre-adolescent females
☐ D   adolescent females have a greater mathematical ability than adolescent males
☐ E   both sexes become less aggressive with increasing age

2.8   Hallucinations

- ☐ A   are misperceptions of an external stimulus
- ☐ B   in the third person are specific for schizophrenia
- ☐ C   rarely occur in both second and third person auditory forms together
- ☐ D   can occur in normal healthy people
- ☐ E   differ from pseudo-hallucinations in not being under voluntary control

2.9   In research design

- ☐ A   a controlled trial suggests that there is a matched control group
- ☐ B   double-blind trials ensure that the experimenters and subjects are not aware to which group the subject belongs
- ☐ C   active placebos are commonly used in double-blind studies
- ☐ D   the placebo effect is negligible in most therapeutic trials
- ☐ E   a stratified sample is less representative of a population than a random sample

2.10   Carl Jung is associated with the following concepts:

- ☐ A   depressive guilt
- ☐ B   electra complex
- ☐ C   collective unconscious
- ☐ D   archetypes
- ☐ E   the shadow

2.11   Schizoid personality disorder is generally considered to include the following characteristics:

- ☐ A   transient psychotic episodes
- ☐ B   excessive self-reference
- ☐ C   eccentricity
- ☐ D   emotional detachment
- ☐ E   withdrawal from close relationships

2.12   The facial nerve

☐   A   innervates muscles of facial expression and mastication
☐   B   is damaged in Bell's palsy
☐   C   contains parasympathetic fibres
☐   D   mediates taste from the posterior third of the tongue
☐   E   innervates the parotid gland

2.13   The neuroleptic malignant syndrome is associated with

☐   A   muscular rigidity
☐   B   autonomic changes
☐   C   neutropenia
☐   D   hypercalcaemia
☐   E   MRI changes

2.14   Thyrotropin releasing hormone (TRH)

☐   A   is found in the spinal cord
☐   B   stimulates sleep
☐   C   reduces blood pressure
☐   D   reduces body temperature
☐   E   increases food consumption

2.15   Recognised side-effects of paroxetine administration include

☐   A   headache
☐   B   salivation
☐   C   sedation
☐   D   nausea
☐   E   priapism

2.16 **Recognised side-effects of tricyclic antidepressants include**

- ☐ A hypothyroidism
- ☐ B cataract
- ☐ C coarse tremor
- ☐ D ileus
- ☐ E hypertension

2.17 **Beta-endorphin is**

- ☐ A released from the pituitary at times of stress
- ☐ B a glycolipid
- ☐ C not a neurotransmitter
- ☐ D localised to layers II and III of the cerebral cortex
- ☐ E involved in the perception of pain

2.18 **The following are true:**

- ☐ A tanycytes line the central canal of the spinal cord
- ☐ B ependymocytes line the fourth ventricle
- ☐ C tanycytes line the lateral ventricles
- ☐ D Schwann cells have tight junctions
- ☐ E fibrous astrocytes have longer and thinner processes compared to protoplasmic astrocytes

2.19 **Cerebellar lesions are associated with**

- ☐ A contralateral pendular reflexes
- ☐ B festinant gait
- ☐ C ipsilateral dysdiadochokinesia
- ☐ D bradykinesia
- ☐ E ipsilateral intention tremor

2.20   The following are true of evoked potential:

☐ A they are the averaged EEG recordings resulting from repeated stimulation in any particular sensory modality
☐ B they consist of only positive components
☐ C visual evoked P100 has increased latency in multiple sclerosis
☐ D auditory evoked P300 abnormalities have been demonstrated in schizophrenia
☐ E early peaks are referred to as endogenous components

2.21   The sympathetic nervous system is characterised by

☐ A unmyelinated preganglionic fibres
☐ B short postganglionic fibres
☐ C contraction of the vas deferens and seminal vesicles
☐ D breakdown of glycogen into glucose
☐ E an ability to stimulate the adrenal medulla to secrete adrenaline and noradrenaline via postganglionic beta receptors

2.22   The following are true:

☐ A GABA is an inhibitory amino acid neurotransmitter
☐ B glutamic acid is a central excitatory neurotransmitter
☐ C aspartic acid is a peripheral excitatory neurotransmitter
☐ D glutamic acid binds to N-methyl-D-aspartate (NMDA) receptors
☐ E NMDA agonists may be useful in epilepsy

2.23   The following are true:

☐ A colloidal antacids decrease absorption of phenothiazines
☐ B fluoxetine increases blood levels of tricyclic antidepressants
☐ C fluvoxamine increases blood levels of warfarin
☐ D carbamazepine decreases blood levels of oral contraceptives
☐ E paroxetine decreases the efficacy of codeine

2.24 **The following figures are correctly associated with the corresponding theories or findings:**

☐ A Murray   neurodevelopmental schizophrenia
☐ B Szasz   ventricular enlargement in chronic schizophrenics
☐ C Crow   Type I and Type II schizophrenia
☐ D Feighner   research and operational diagnostic criteria
☐ E Andresen   positive and negative symptoms of schizophrenia

2.25 **Features of Liddle's disorganisation syndrome include**

☐ A poverty of content of speech
☐ B unchanging facial expression
☐ C hallucinations
☐ D inappropriate affect
☐ E incoherent speech

2.26 **The following are correctly associated:**

☐ A Fromm–Reichmann   schizo-affective psychosis
☐ B Mayer–Gross   oneirophrenia
☐ C Langfeldt   latent schizophrenia
☐ D Wynn and Singer   defective communication
☐ E Hoch and Polatin   pseudoneurotic schizophrenia

2.27 **Schizophrenia is associated with the following:**

☐ A tuberculosis
☐ B rheumatoid arthritis
☐ C suicide
☐ D obstetric complications at birth
☐ E substance misuse

2.28   In schizophrenia, factors associated with a poor outcome include

- ☐ A   residing in a developing country
- ☐ B   acute onset of illness
- ☐ C   identifiable precipitant
- ☐ D   being unemployed
- ☐ E   ventricular dilatation

2.29   Brown's original vulnerability factors identified in the 1978 Camberwell Study

- ☐ A   include caring for young children
- ☐ B   include working outside the home
- ☐ C   include loss of mother by death or separation before the age of fifteen.
- ☐ D   include divorce
- ☐ E   the Outer Hebrides Study (1981) confirmed the findings of the Camberwell Study

2.30   Depression is associated with

- ☐ A   blunted prolactin response to apomorphine
- ☐ B   blunted somatotropin response to clonidine
- ☐ C   hypercortisolaemia
- ☐ D   loss of circadian rhythm
- ☐ E   blunted ACTH response to corticotrophin

2.31   With regard to seasonal affective disorder (SAD)

- ☐ A   there are no gender differences
- ☐ B   it is associated with carbohydrate craving
- ☐ C   the diagnosis was originally based on Rosenthal's criterion
- ☐ D   treatment is best given in the morning
- ☐ E   the response to treatment is slow

2.32   With regard to deliberate self-harm

☐   A   5% commit suicide in the first year
☐   B   deliberate self-poisoning accounts for 90%
☐   C   50% of suicides have a history of deliberate self-harm
☐   D   it is most common in middle aged females of low social class
☐   E   there is no gender difference beyond the age of fifty

2.33   Obsessive-compulsive disorder is associated with

☐   A   onset in later adult life
☐   B   prevalence of 2–5%
☐   C   increased incidence in females
☐   D   Gilles de la Tourette syndrome
☐   E   increased prevalence in relatives

2.34   Predisposing social factors that may induce vulnerability to depressive illness are as follows

☐   A   unemployment
☐   B   one or more children under the age of 14 years at home
☐   C   the loss of mother before the age of 11 years
☐   D   lack of a confiding relationship
☐   E   being in a single parent family

2.35   Abnormalities of the following neurotransmitter systems have been implicated in schizophrenia:

☐   A   serotonin
☐   B   dopamine
☐   C   noradrenaline
☐   D   acetylcholine
☐   E   glutamate

2.36   Recognised features of Wernicke's encephalopathy include

☐ A   vitamin B12 deficiency
☐ B   loss of hearing
☐ C   clear consciousness
☐ D   nystagmus
☐ E   ataxia

2.37   Amphetamines

☐ A   stimulate appetite
☐ B   are used to treat narcolepsy
☐ C   overdose results in hypothermia
☐ D   use is associated with paranoid psychosis
☐ E   are prescribed to hyperkinetic hyperactive children

2.38   Delirium is a characteristic of the following conditions:

☐ A   organic toxic states
☐ B   delirium tremens
☐ C   alcoholic hallucinosis
☐ D   Korsakoff's syndrome
☐ E   Wernicke's encephalopathy

2.39   The following are characteristics of Jakob-Creutzfeldt disease:

☐ A   the peak age of onset in the classical form is in the third or
        fourth decade
☐ B   this can resemble an autosomal dominant disorder running in
        families
☐ C   the transmissible agent may be a prion protein
☐ D   spongiform encephalopathy with vacuolation is seen in
        cerebral grey matter on CT examination
☐ E   most patients die within two years of onset

2.40   In relatives of patients with alcohol dependence

☐   A   there is a 2-fold increase of risk of alcoholism in first-degree
        relatives
☐   B   sons of alcoholics are more likely to become alcoholic if
        raised by their biological parents than if adopted by non-
        alcoholic parents
☐   C   there are higher rates of childhood conduct disorder in sons of
        alcoholic parents
☐   D   there is likely to be increased alcoholism if the patient has
        Cloninger type 1 alcoholism
☐   E   there is equal monozygotic and dizygotic concordance for
        alcoholism

2.41   Recognised causes of dementia include

☐   A   Parkinson's disease
☐   B   vitamin B12 deficiency
☐   C   alcohol dependence syndrome
☐   D   thyroid disease
☐   E   depressive illness

2.42   Diagnostic features of childhood autism include

☐   A   language retardation
☐   B   depressed mood
☐   C   ritualistic and compulsive behaviour
☐   D   seizures
☐   E   failure to develop social relationships

2.43   School refusal is associated with

☐   A   social class IV and V
☐   B   antisocial behaviour
☐   C   below average academic achievement
☐   D   dysfunctional family and inconsistent parenting
☐   E   truancy

2.44   The following are disorders of lipid metabolism:

☐ A   Tay–Sachs disease
☐ B   Niemann–Pick disease
☐ C   Von Gierke's disease
☐ D   Gaucher's disease
☐ E   Sanfilippo syndrome

2.45   In anorexia nervosa

☐ A   even with restoration of normal body weight, amenorrhoea
         persists in 50%
☐ B   testosterone levels are normal in women
☐ C   T3 levels are significantly reduced
☐ D   there is increased release of antidiuretic hormone
☐ E   the metabolic clearance of cortisol is reduced

2.46   Puerperal psychosis

☐ A   is more likely to occur in women with a history of bipolar
         affective disorder
☐ B   is classified under schizophrenia, schizotypal and delusional
         disorders in ICD-10
☐ C   occurs in approximately 1 in 5,000 births
☐ D   is associated with primigravida
☐ E   increases the risk of future psychotic episodes

**2.47   The following are recognised associations of anorexia
         nervosa:**

☐ A   oestrogen deficiency and osteoporosis
☐ B   hypokalaemia and cardiac arrhythmias
☐ C   increased white cell count
☐ D   increased growth hormone levels
☐ E   secondary sexual characteristics are absent

2.48 **Criteria of dependent personality disorder as defined by ICD-10 include**

- ☐ A persistent and pervasive feelings of tension and apprehension
- ☐ B unwillingness even to make reasonable demands on the people one depends on
- ☐ C preoccupation with fears of being left to care for oneself
- ☐ D restrictions in lifestyle because of need for physical security
- ☐ E limited capacity to make everyday decisions without an excessive amount of advice and reassurance from others

2.49 **Characteristic features of Latah include**

- ☐ A it affects predominantly females
- ☐ B echopraxia
- ☐ C sexual promiscuity
- ☐ D automatic obedience
- ☐ E occurence mainly in Latin American countries

2.50 **Specific delusional disorders include**

- ☐ A folie a deux
- ☐ B Cotard's syndrome
- ☐ C Fregoli syndrome
- ☐ D Capgras syndrome
- ☐ E erotomania

MULTIPLE CHOICE QUESTION PAPER 2 – ANSWERS

2.1   **Answers: A C E**

Eysenck's type theory uses an orthogonal approach (i.e. second order factor analysis to identify a small number of powerful independent factors) whereas Cattel's trait theory uses an oblique approach (i.e. first order factor analysis to identify a large number of less powerful factors which are correlated to some degree (non-independent)).

2.2   **Answers: B C D**

Psychoanalytic theories of personality imply active forces within an individual, either conscious or unconscious, are the inner determinants of behaviour.

2.3   **Answer: A**

Using Q sort the rater compares traits within an individual. Personal disposition and individuality can be identified. Reliability can be assessed using two Q sorts.

2.4   **Answers: A B E**

Tonic alertness reflects intrinsic changes in the level of arousal. The orientating response occurs in phasic alertness and involves a decrease in both heart rate and respiratory rate in the presence of a desynchronised EEG.

2.5   **Answers: B D**

Sensory memory lasts 0.5 seconds and is located within the receiving sensory system. Auditory information sensory memory is called echoic. Haptic memory concerns sensory information from touch.

2.6   **Answers: A B D E**

Babbling is independent of learning or culture and begins at six to nine months.

2.7   **Answers: A B E**

Boys develop greater visuo-spatial and mathematical ability than girls post-adolescence.

2.8   **Answer: D**

Hallucinations are defined as perceptions in the absence of an external stimulus. Illusions are misperceptions of external stimuli. Auditory hallucinations in the second and third person occur together commonly in schizophrenia and less frequently in affective disorders. Hypnopompic and hypnogogic hallucinations occur in normal healthy people on waking and sleeping, respectively. Pseudohallucinations differ from hallucinations because they occur within the mind rather than in external space.

2.9   **Answers: A B**

Double-blind randomised controlled trials are the gold standard of treatment studies, the control group should be adequately matched, the blinded design should prevent any experimenter bias and both together should reduce any effect of the placebo effect which is often marked in treatment studies. The use of active placebos, containing active elements to induce side-effects similar to the experimental drug, is relatively rare. A stratified sample is generally more representative as it takes random samples of sub-populations.

2.10   **Answers: C D E**

Jung divided the psyche into the conscious persona and the personal and collective unconscious. Archetypes including self, hero, wise old man, animus and anima were inborn predispositions to perceive and act in a certain manner. Complexes are associated ideas, a mix of the persona and archetypes that can dictate acts and feelings in certain situations. The shadow is the repressed opposite of the persona, a composite of disliked elements.

2.11   **Answers: C D E**

This includes emotional coldness and detachment; withdrawal from close relationships and an autistic preference for fantasy; and eccentricity.

2.12   **Answers: B C**

The facial nerve innervates muscles of facial expression. The sensory component innervates taste from the anterior two-thirds of the tongue and parasympathetic fibres innervate the submaxillary and sublingual glands. The trigeminal nerve innervates masticatory muscles whilst the glossopharyngeal nerve innervates the posterior third of the tongue and the parotid gland.

2.13   **Answers: A B**

This is thought to occur with exposure to any antipsychotic; with onset within 2–28 days of exposure. Its characteristic features are muscular rigidity, akinesia, pyrexia, clouded consciousness and autonomic changes. Investigations show neutrophilia, raised CPK, secondary electrolyte disturbances (reduced calcium, magnesium and phosphate) and slow waves on EEG. There are no CSF changes and the MRI is normal.

2.14   **Answer: A**

Thyrotropin releasing hormone (TRH) is found throughout the CNS. It has a general antidepressant effect, inhibiting sleep and increasing body temperature and blood pressure. It decreases food consumption.

2.15   **Answers: A C D**

Side-effects include dry mouth, sedation, headache, nausea and vomiting.

2.16   **Answers: D E**

The tremor associated with tricyclic antidepressant use is usually a fine tremor.

2.17   **Answers: A D E**

Beta-endorphin is a peptide neurotransmitter found throughout the brain that is released in response to stress and is involved in the perception of pain.

2.18   **Answers: B E**

Ependymocytes line the ventricles and spinal cord except the floor of the third ventricle over the median eminence which is lined by tanycytes.

2.19   **Answers: C E**

Cerebellar lesions cause ipsilateral signs due to a double cross-over before and after synapsing in the red nucleus. The signs are primarily poor co-ordination (ataxia, slurred speech and intention tremor) in cerebellar hemisphere lesions. Mid-line or vermis cerebellar lesions cause abnormalities in posture such as titubation (a staggering and stumbling gait with shaking of the trunk and head) broad based gait and Romberg's sign (difficulty in standing erect with feet approximated and eyes closed). Festinant gait and bradykinesia is seen in Parkinson's disease. Pendular reflexes are observed ipsilaterally.

2.20   **Answers: A C D**

Evoked potentials are thought to represent slow synaptic activity and are obtained by averaging a series of EEG recordings in any particular modality (e.g. auditory, visual, somatosensory) to increase signal:noise ratios. Positive (P) and negative (N) components reflect positive and negative changes in electrical currents in response to a particular stimulus with respect to time in milliseconds. Early peaks are exogenous, late peaks are endogenous and are more susceptible to internal factors e.g. attention.

2.21   **Answers: C D**

The adrenal medulla is essentially a sympathetic ganglion whereby postganglionic cells have lost their axons and have become specialised by secreting directly into the blood-stream. The cholinergic preganglionic neurones have become the secretomotor supply via muscarinic receptors. Sympathetic neurones typically have short myelinated preganglionic fibres and long unmyelinated postganglionic fibres.

2.22   **Answers: A B D**

Glutamate and aspartate are both excitatory amino acid neuro-transmitters found in the brain. NMDA receptor antagonists have anxiolytic and anticonvulsant properties.

2.23   **Answers: All true**

Psychotropic medication interactions arise because of their chemical properties and effects on metabolism. It is important to be aware of these in clinical practice.

2.24   **Answers: A C D E**

Szasz belonged to the anti-psychiatry school and described schizo-phrenia as an understandable response to stresses and pressures within the individual's family and society as a whole. Ventricular enlargement in the brains of chronic schizophrenics was noted by Johnston in 1976 using CT.

2.25   **Answers: A D E**

The other symptoms are more characteristic of psychomotor poverty and reality distortion.

2.26   **Answers: B D E**

Fromm–Reichmann described the schizophrenogenic mother. Schizo-affective psychosis was used by Kasanin. Langfeldt coined the term schizophreniform psychosis.

2.27   **Answers: All true**

The association with rheumatoid arthritis is negative, but there is an association. The risk of deliberate self-harm is increased and so is the risk of completed suicide. Co-morbidity is a big problem, particularly concomitant substance misuse.

2.28   **Answers: D E**

Factors associated with an unfavourable outcome include living in a developed country, having low socio-economic status, and insidious onset with predominantly negative symptoms. Poor compliance and response to treatment are also associated with an unfavourable outcome.

2.29   **Answer: A**

The Camberwell Study (Brown and Harris) identified four vulner-ability factors i.e. not working outside the home, loss of mother by death or separation before the age of eleven, having no one to confide in. The Outer Hebrides Study (Brown and Proudo) conducted in a rural community failed to confirm the findings of the Camberwell Study except caring for three children under the age of fourteen years.

2.30   **Answers: All true**

Hypercortisolaemia is thought to be due to hypersecretion of CRF resulting in a blunted ACTH response to CRF. Dexamethasone non-suppression occurs in up to 50% of depressed patients. This is a non-specific marker as non-suppression also occurs in anorexia nervosa, alcoholism, obsessive compulsive disorder (OCD) and schizophrenia. Non-suppression can be affected by factors such as drugs, ECT, endocrine disorders, age and changes in body mass. Thus dexamethasone non-suppression is not a useful test of depression or a useful response to treatment in depression.

2.31   **Answers: B C D**

Rosenthal's original criterion of seasonality was that major depression should be present in at least two consecutive previous years during autumn or winter and remit in the following spring or summer. SAD is characteristically atypical in terms of symptoms with hypersomnia, weight gain and carbohydrate craving. Treatment is as for other forms of depression with the addition of light treatment in those whose depression is only present in winter. Bright artificial daylight of 2500 lux should be given in the morning and late evening. The response is extremely rapid with a 50% reduction in symptoms within four days. Relapse is also rapid on discontinuing light treatment, therefore it should be continued throughout winter months.

2.32   **Answers: B C**

Deliberate self-harm is most common in young, low social class females with a gender ratio of 2:1 compared with young, low social class males. The gender ratio equalises by the age of fifty. Risk is correlated to socio-economic deprivation, alcoholism and person-ality disorders. Most episodes are preceded by a major life event, often serious interpersonal difficulties with a partner or friend. 1% commit suicide in the first year and the risk remains elevated for up to five years. 10% ultimately commit suicide.

2.33   **Answers: D E**

This is a rare disorder (prevalence 0.01–0.2%). It occurs usually in early adult life, rarely after age 45. It has a genetic contribution with 5–7% of parents affected; sex incidence is equal and there is an association with Gilles de la Tourette syndrome.

2.34   **Answers: A C D**

Studies by Brown and Harris suggested the following vulnerability factors for depressive illness in women: lack of a confiding relationship; unemployment; three or more children under the age of 14 years at home; loss of mother before the age of 11 years.

2.35   **Answers: A B E**

The dopamine overactivity theory has been based on the response to dopamine blocking drugs. More recent interest fuelled by clozapine's action has suggested serotonin plays an important role; this has been reflected in the development of the new atypical antipsychotics. There is some recent evidence to show that the glutamate system may also be involved. There is little evidence to support acetylcholine or noradrenaline involvement.

2.36   **Answers: D E**

Wernicke's encephalopathy occurs because of vitamin B1 deficiency and is characterised by the development of symptoms of confusion, nystagmus, ataxia and ocular palsies.

2.37   **Answers: B D E**

Amphetamines increase well-being and stimulate activity. They reduce appetite and were initially used as anorectics. Tolerance develops rapidly and in overdose they produce arrhythmias and hyperpyrexia. Amphetamine use is associated with 'amphetamine psychosis' that is akin to paranoid schizophrenia. Amphetamines are also occasionally used to treat nocturnal enuresis.

2.38   **Answers: A B E**

Delirium is a state of altered consciousness, in which there is confusion and disorientation for time, place and sometimes person. Delirium is a characteristic of acute or subacute organic conditions such as toxic states, delirium tremens and Wernicke's encephalopathy. This is not the case in alcoholic hallucinosis or Korsakoff's syndrome, which occur in clear consciousness.

2.39 Answers: B C E

Jakob-Creutzfeldt disease is one of two human spongiform encephalopathies. The peak age of onset in the classical case is in the 60s and 70s. Initially it presents with personality changes followed by a confusional state progressing to dementia. It is a rare disease, incidence 0.3 to 5 per million, with an unidentified transmissible agent, most likely a prion. Neuro-pathological findings show spongiform vacuolation of grey matter. There are few gross CT/MRI changes; a characteristic EEG finding showing a large generalised periodic spike with slow wave complexes. The EEG changes are different in the new variant JC disease that affects individuals under 30 years of age and may be related to bovine spongiform encephalopathy.

2.40 Answer: C

There is a 7-fold increase in alcoholism in first-degree relatives. There is higher concordance in monozygotic twins than in dizygotic (70%:43%) males. The sons of alcoholics are four times more likely to become alcoholic regardless of being brought up by their parents or adopted. Sons of alcoholics have higher rates of conduct disorder. Cloninger divided alcoholics into 2 groups; type 1 were less genetically predisposed and had more guilt whilst type 2 were more likely to be male, have a stronger genetic loading and have more impulsive/antisocial traits.

2.41 Answers: A B C D

Causes of secondary dementia include CNS pathology including stroke, syphilis, normal pressure hydrocephalus, Parkinson's disease; vitamin deficiencies including folic acid and B12; Toxic ingestion of alcohol and heavy metals; metabolic and endocrine disease including liver and thyroid disease; and autoimmune disorders including SLE. Depression does not cause dementia but can mimic it and this is often referred to as depressive pseudodementia.

2.42 Answers: C D E

Childhood autism is more common in males, large families and lower socio-economic classes.

2.43   **Answers: All false**
The factors listed are associated with or are features of truancy.
School refusal is associated with normal to high standard of
academic achievement and overprotective parenting.

2.44   **Answers: A B D**
Von Gierke's disease is a glycogen storage disease (glucose-6-
phosphatase deficiency). It has autosomal recessive inheritance.
Sanfilippo syndrome is a connective tissue disorder.

2.45   **Answers: A B C E**
T3 levels are reduced by 50% and testosterone levels in men are
lowered but not in women. The reduction in release of ADH leads
to the development of nephrogenic diabetes. ACTH levels are
normal.

2.46   **Answers: A D E**
Puerperal psychosis occurs in 1:500 births. Onset is usually within
1–3 weeks postpartum and duration is approximately 6–12 weeks.
The presentation is usually that of an affective psychosis and a
history of bipolar disorder increases the likelihood of puerperal
psychosis to 20%. The disorder is poorly defined and not clearly
specified in ICD-10 or DSM IV. Following an episode of puerperal
psychosis, the risk of a future episode is 1 in 5 and the likelihood of
psychotic episodes at any time is also significantly increased.

2.47   **Answers: A B D**
The clinical signs in anorexia may reveal dry skin with lanugo hair.
Hypothermia, hypotension and bradycardia may be present.
Oestrogen deficiency causes osteoporosis. Starvation and purging
cause hypokalaemia. The white cell count is low. There is increased
basal cortisol with elevated growth hormone levels due to carbohydrate restriction. Gonadotrophins are reduced but secondary
sexual characteristics are retained.

2.48   **Answers: B C E**

Persistent and pervasive feelings of tension, apprehension and restrictions in lifestyle because of need for physical security are features of avoidant personality disorder. Criteria of dependent personality disorder include subordination of one's own needs to those of others and undue compliance with their wishes. Feeling uncomfortable or helpless when alone because of exaggerated fears of inability to care for oneself, and encouraging or allowing others to make most of one's important life decisions.

2.49   **Answers: A B D**

Latah occurs at times of stress and is observed predominantly in the Far East and Africa. It results in suggestibility and echolalia and is described as an hysterical illness.

2.50   **Answers: All true**

Also includes pathological jealousy (Othello syndrome). Cotard's syndrome is a nihilistic delusional disorder in which the patient believes that parts of their body do not exist or that they have suddenly lost their friends, family or money. Capgras syndrome is a delusional disorder in which the patient believes that a familiar person has been replaced by an exact double. Fregoli syndrome is different in that the patient believes that a familiar person has taken on different appearances. In Folie a deux two or more people share a delusional disorder. Erotomania is also a delusional disorder in which the patient believes that an individual, usually of higher status or fame, is in love with them.

MULTIPLE CHOICE QUESTION PAPER 3

50 questions: time allowed 1 hour 30 minutes

3.1   The following are true of Eysenck's type theory of personality:

☐ A   introversion-extroversion is assumed to be normally distributed
☐ B   the biological correlate of neuroticism is the reticular activating system
☐ C   psychoticism is not normally distributed
☐ D   the Eysenck Personality Inventory (EPI) includes a lie scale
☐ E   the Eysenck Personality Questionnaire (EPQ) includes a psychoticism scale

3.2   Defence mechanisms

☐ A   are used by the id
☐ B   are conscious
☐ C   are disadvantageous
☐ D   were proposed by Adler
☐ E   protect against conflict

3.3   With regard to emotion

☐ A   Ekman has identified six universal primary emotions
☐ B   Schacter proposed the cognitive labelling theory
☐ C   cognitive appraisal does not affect the quality or intensity of an emotion
☐ D   cognitive appraisal is necessary for emotion to be experienced
☐ E   cognitive labelling proposes that autonomic arousal is variable in emotion

3.4   Criticisms of an ethological theory of human aggression proposed by Lorenz include that

☐ A   early man was a hunter gatherer rather than a warrior
☐ B   other primates also kill each other
☐ C   aggression in animals is generally considered to be reactive rather than spontaneous
☐ D   it does not account for learning
☐ E   the theory is based on the study of non-primates

3.5   Short-term memory

☐ A   has a capacity of 7 + 2 units
☐ B   the capacity can be expanded by chunking
☐ C   has duration of 0.5 seconds
☐ D   encoding is primarily iconic
☐ E   rehearsal is easily disrupted

3.6   In colour vision

☐ A   rods are essential
☐ B   the sum of the red, blue and green wavelengths determine colour in the trichromatic light theory
☐ C   the trichromatic theory implies that every colour, including white, excites red, blue and green cones in a characteristic ratio
☐ D   the opponent colour theory has a tetrachromic basis
☐ E   colour-blindness is consistent with the opponent theory

3.7   With regard to gender

☐ A   basic gender identity is established by the age of three years
☐ B   homosexuals have normal gender identity
☐ C   gender stability is established by the age of six years
☐ D   gender constancy is established during adolescent turmoil
☐ E   transsexuals have abnormal gender identity

3.8 **The following are disorders of the content of speech:**

☐ A neologisms
☐ B dysarthria
☐ C dysphasia
☐ D word salad
☐ E pareidolia

3.9 **The following types of hallucination are correctly characterised:**

☐ A extracampine hallucination occurs when awaking from sleep
☐ B reduplicative hallucination occurs repeatedly in exactly the same fashion
☐ C functional hallucinations serve a specific purpose
☐ D reflex hallucination occurs automatically without any associated trigger
☐ E pseudohallucination, that which is intangible and located in inner subjective space and lacks substantiality

3.10 **The following concepts are paired with the appropriate person:**

☐ A Karl Abraham: early and late anal stages
☐ B Hartmann: ego-psychology
☐ C Winnicott: transitional objects
☐ D Adler: life tasks
☐ E Anna Freud: good enough mother

3.11 **Hysterical or histrionic personality disorder is generally considered to include the following characteristics:**

☐ A misconstruing neutral actions as hostile
☐ B persistently manipulative
☐ C suggestibility
☐ D self dramatisation
☐ E indecisiveness and doubt

3.12   Extrapyramidal symptoms can arise secondary to disorders of the

☐ A   cerebellum
☐ B   basal ganglia
☐ C   corticospinal tracts
☐ D   dopaminergic system
☐ E   noradrenergic system

3.13   Lithium

☐ A   is protein bound
☐ B   can cause hypo- and hyper-thyroidism
☐ C   is excreted and unmetabolised by the kidney
☐ D   is excreted in saliva
☐ E   should not be prescribed with thiazide diuretics

3.14   Cholecystokinin (CCK)

☐ A   exists in the brain predominantly as an eight amino acid
          fragment
☐ B   produces analgesia
☐ C   facilitates sleep
☐ D   reduces food intake
☐ E   is often co-localised with dopamine

3.15   Features of lithium toxicity include

☐ A   tremor
☐ B   confusion
☐ C   ataxia
☐ D   exophthalmos
☐ E   dysarthria

3.16   Drugs that can cause depression include

☐ A propranolol
☐ B cimetidine
☐ C methyldopa
☐ D frusemide
☐ E digoxin

3.17   The Papez circuit includes

☐ A the posterior nucleus of the thalamus
☐ B corpus callosum
☐ C cingulate gyrus
☐ D epithalamus
☐ E hippocampus

3.18   The oculomotor nerve

☐ A has sensory and motor components
☐ B supplies the superior oblique
☐ C carries post-ganglionic parasympathetic fibres to the ciliary
       ganglion
☐ D is affected in Benedikt's syndrome
☐ E does not pass through the cavernous sinus

3.19   The following occur during the action potential of a neurone:

☐ A sodium influx
☐ B potassium influx
☐ C chloride efflux
☐ D intracellular voltage becomes more negative
☐ E calcium influx

3.20   Concerning sleep

- ☐ A   stage two sleep is characterised by sleep spindles
- ☐ B   REM sleep occurs during light sleep
- ☐ C   saw tooth waves occur in stage 3 and 4 sleep
- ☐ D   REM sleep decreases with age
- ☐ E   kappa complexes are transient waves of 12 to 14 Hz lasting approximately 0.5 seconds

3.21   The following are intermediate in the biosynthesis of noradrenaline:

- ☐ A   3,4,dihydroxyphenylalanine
- ☐ B   tryptophan
- ☐ C   adrenaline
- ☐ D   phenylethylamine
- ☐ E   tyrosine

3.22   The following are true of opioids:

- ☐ A   enkephalins are five chain amino acids
- ☐ B   enkephalins are derived from peptide precursors
- ☐ C   craving is mediated by the mu opioid receptor
- ☐ D   enkephalins are endogenous opioids
- ☐ E   nalorphine is a kappa opioid receptor agonist

3.23   In the EEG

- ☐ A   alpha waves are greater than 13 Hz
- ☐ B   delta waves are more prominent posteriorly
- ☐ C   delta waves are of high amplitude
- ☐ D   lambda waves are pathological
- ☐ E   sharp waves have a duration of less than 80 milliseconds

3.24   Schizophrenia

☐ A   has a point prevalence of 1%
☐ B   occurs more often in males
☐ C   is more common in urban populations
☐ D   is associated with right handedness
☐ E   accounts for 40% of all suicides

3.25   Characteristics of schizophreniform psychosis in epilepsy include

☐ A   preservation of affective response
☐ B   onset preceding that of epilepsy by 2–3 years
☐ C   absence of a family history of schizophrenia
☐ D   history of personality disorder
☐ E   association with a dominant hemisphere ictal focus

3.26   Indicators of good prognosis in schizophrenia include

☐ A   flattening of affect
☐ B   poverty of speech
☐ C   family history of affective disorder
☐ D   presence of precipitating event
☐ E   acute onset

3.27   Male schizophrenics are more likely to have

☐ A   structural brain abnormalities
☐ B   had complications at birth
☐ C   a genetic predisposition
☐ D   a better prognosis
☐ E   onset at a young age

3.28   Recognised features of cycloid psychoses include

☐   A   sudden onset
☐   B   poor short-term and long-term prognosis
☐   C   overwhelming anxiety
☐   D   disorientation
☐   E   paranoid delusions

3.29   Bi-polar disorder

☐   A   is more common in females
☐   B   has a lifetime prevalence of 1%
☐   C   is associated with an increased risk of bi-polar disorder in relatives
☐   D   is associated with an increased risk of uni-polar disorder in relatives
☐   E   never occurs for the first time after the age of sixty-five years

3.30   Evidence supporting the monoaminergic hypothesis of mood disorders includes the following:

☐   A   CSF 5-HIAA concentration is not generally decreased in depression
☐   B   low CSF 5-HIAA concentration has been reported in post-mortem studies of suicide
☐   C   CSF noradrenaline concentration is not generally decreased in depression
☐   D   increased serotonin platelet receptor binding has been reported in the cortex in post-mortem studies of suicide
☐   E   decreased plasma tryptophan has been reported in depression

3.31   Suicide

☐   A   accounts for 5% of all deaths per year
☐   B   is increased in anaesthetists
☐   C   is increased in general hospital in-patients
☐   D   is decreased in prison inmates
☐   E   is rare in adolescence

3.32   Absolute contraindications for ECT include

☐   A   pulmonary disease
☐   B   raised intracranial pressure
☐   C   recent myocardial infarction
☐   D   pregnancy
☐   E   epilepsy

3.33   Post-traumatic stress disorder (PTSD) is associated with

☐   A   exposure to an event within the range of usual human
          experience
☐   B   intrusive recollection of the traumatic event
☐   C   survivor guilt
☐   D   a previous family history of psychiatric disease
☐   E   alcohol or drug abuse

3.34   The following occur commonly during manic illness:

☐   A   grandiose ideas and delusions
☐   B   first rank schizophrenic symptoms
☐   C   auditory hallucinations
☐   D   visual hallucinations
☐   E   irritability

3.35   Recognised features of Korsakoff's psychosis include

- ☐ A   difficulty in new learning
- ☐ B   confabulation
- ☐ C   pyridoxine deficiency
- ☐ D   apathy
- ☐ E   retrograde amnesia

3.36   Glue-sniffing

- ☐ A   is more common in boys
- ☐ B   is associated with visual hallucinations
- ☐ C   rapidly leads to physical dependence
- ☐ D   is associated with aggressive behaviour
- ☐ E   is responsible for about 1% of deaths in teenagers

3.37   Memory loss is associated with

- ☐ A   confabulation
- ☐ B   dissociative amnesias
- ☐ C   Cotard's syndrome
- ☐ D   déjà vu phenomena
- ☐ E   extracampine hallucinations

3.38   Hydrocephalus

- ☐ A   with normal pressure is a treatable cause of dementia
- ☐ B   is characterised by gait disturbance
- ☐ C   is associated with a history of subarachnoid haemorrhage
- ☐ D   is associated with incontinence
- ☐ E   can be due to brain atrophy

3.39 **Clinical features of the alcohol dependency syndrome, as defined by Edwards and Gross, include**

☐ A lack of awareness of compulsion to drink
☐ B increased tolerance to alcohol
☐ C prominence of drink seeking behaviour
☐ D reinstatement after abstinence
☐ E varied pattern of drinking

3.40 **Characteristics more suggestive of pseudodementia than dementia are**

☐ A gradual onset
☐ B a history of dementia in the family
☐ C impaired ability to learn new material
☐ D behaviour inconsistent with progressive dementia
☐ E lack of response to antidepressant medication

3.41 **In the treatment of sexual dysfunction the following are associated with good outcome**

☐ A hypochondriacal neurosis
☐ B vaginismus
☐ C premature ejaculation
☐ D acute onset in a healthy relationship
☐ E diminished libido

3.42 **Conduct disorder**

☐ A is associated with specific reading retardation
☐ B is also described as delinquency
☐ C has a good prognosis
☐ D is relatively rare
☐ E is almost exclusively a disorder of boys

3.43 Down's syndrome is associated with

☐ A chronic blepharitis
☐ B lens dislocation
☐ C Brushfield's spots
☐ D hypertelorism
☐ E epicanthic folds

3.44 Gastrointestinal complications of anorexia nervosa include

☐ A duodenal dilatation
☐ B constipation
☐ C steatorrhoea
☐ D parotid enlargement
☐ E oesophagitis

3.45 Features of non-organic failure to thrive include

☐ A presentation in first year of life
☐ B no evidence of physical ill-health or cognitive delay
☐ C irritability
☐ D lethargy
☐ E apathy

3.46 Masters and Johnson described the following five stages in the normal sexual response:

☐ A desire influenced by social and hormonal factors
☐ B excitement followed by appropriate physiological changes
☐ C plateau as physiological changes and excitement are maintained
☐ D orgasm with increased parasympathetic activity
☐ E resolution, with the refractory period increasing with age in men

3.47 **The following statements regarding the England and Wales 1983 Mental Health Act are correct:**

☐ A part IV concerns consent to treatment
☐ B guardianship is considered in part I
☐ C the Act does not use the term mental retardation
☐ D mental illness is clearly defined
☐ E the Act has six parts and 83 sections

3.48 **Social consequences of mental disorder include**

☐ A restricted social networks
☐ B stigma
☐ C poverty
☐ D isolation
☐ E avoidance and withdrawal

3.49 **Delusions**

☐ A occur in severe depression
☐ B cannot be shaken by reason
☐ C are usually shared within a particular cultural group
☐ D are described as simple, complex and sophisticated
☐ E are beliefs that are invariably false

3.50 **Features of catatonia include**

☐ A catalepsy
☐ B echopraxia
☐ C pareidolia
☐ D mutism
☐ E negativism

MULTIPLE CHOICE QUESTION PAPER 3 – ANSWERS

3.1   **Answers: A C D E**

Neuroticism is also normally distributed. The biological correlate is the sympathetic branch of the autonomic nervous system and its interaction with the limbic system. The reticular activating system is a biological correlate of introversion-extroversion. Androgen has been suggested to be the biological correlate of psychoticism.

3.2   **Answer: E**

Defence mechanisms are unconscious and help to alleviate anxiety, being advantageous in the short term. They were proposed by Sigmund Freud and elaborated by Anna Freud.

3.3   **Answers: A B**

In cognitive labelling, autonomic arousal is similar but it is the interpretation of that arousal that is important in determining the emotion experienced.

3.4   **Answers: A C D E**

Although most primate behaviour is peaceful, primates are known to kill each other and this favours the theory proposed by Lorenz.

3.5   **Answers: A B E**

Chunking involves categorising a large chunk of information to smaller amounts using a recognition code. Encoding is primarily echoic and rehearsal can be disrupted by internal or external stimuli.

3.6   **Answers: C D E**

In the trichromatic light theory the sum of the red, blue and green wavelengths determines brightness. Colour is determined by the ratio of the wavelengths. The opponent colour theory is based on two receptors i.e. red/green and yellow/blue.

3.7   **Answers: A B C E**

Gender constancy over time and across situations is developed by the age of seven.

3.8   **Answers: A C D**

Neologisms are new words, or idiosyncratic use of real words, usually seen in schizophrenia. Dysarthria is a disorder of speech production, whilst dysphasia is a disorder of the speech content. Word salad is the description of incomprehensibly broken speech content and pareidolia is vivid visual images seen while looking at diffuse stimuli.

3.9   **Answer: E**

Extracampine hallucinations occur outside the individual's field of perception. Reduplicative hallucinations involve the experience of an additional limb or body part. With functional hallucinations both the normal percept and the hallucination that it produces are experienced simultaneously. Reflex hallucinations are those that occur in one sensory modality in response to stimulation in another.

3.10   **Answers: A B C D**

Abraham refined the Freudian psychosexual basis of development into early and later stages. Hartmann viewed the ego as autonomous and developed ego-psychology in the USA. Winnicott coined the term 'good enough mother' and the transitional object used as a comfort in the mother's absence. Adler proposed man as a social creature, striving for success in the areas of life tasks, society, work and sex.

3.11   **Answers: B C D**

Hysterical or histrionic personality disorder includes self-dramatisation and exaggerated expression of emotions; persistently manipulative; and suggestibility.

3.12   **Answers: A B D**

The extrapyramidal system refers to motor control outside the influence of the corticospinal tracts. This leaves the basal ganglia and cerebellar systems. Basal ganglia depletion of dopamine, either iatrogenic through use of traditional antipsychotics or in Parkinson's disease, results in extrapyramidal signs: akinesia, muscular rigidity and tremor.

3.13   **Answers: B C D E**

Lithium is a salt and as such has no protein binding and is excreted via the kidneys unchanged. It is excreted to some degree in saliva as its excretion follows that of sodium, thiazide diuretic use tends to increase plasma levels. It has a narrow therapeutic range and toxicity can be fatal. Longer-term use can cause hypothyroidism and more rarely hyperthyroidism.

3.14   **Answers: All true**

It is more potent than morphine as an analgesic. Cholecystokinin also produces hypothermia.

3.15   **Answers: A B C E**

When lithium levels rise above 2.0 mmol/l signs of toxicity may occur. These include tremor, ataxia, incoordination, slurring of speech, disorientation, confusion, and convulsions.

3.16   **Answers: All true**

Other drugs that can cause depression include: reserpine, phenothiazines and clonidine.

3.17   **Answers: C E**

The Papez circuit includes the cingulate gyrus, the hippocampus, hypothalamus, mamillary body and anterior nucleus of the thalamus.

3.18   **Answer: D**

The oculomotor nerve is the third cranial nerve and supplies all extrinsic ocular muscles except the superior oblique (fourth nerve) and the lateral rectus (sixth nerve). It carries pre-ganglionic parasympathetic fibres from the Edinger Westphal nucleus to the ciliary ganglion and sympathetic fibres to Mueller's muscle. It also supplies levator palpebrae superioris.

3.19   **Answer: A**

Resting potential is approximately -70 mV due to Na-K ATPase and greater membrane permeability to potassium ions relative to sodium ions. De-polarisation during an action potential leads to a rapid sodium ion influx via voltage gated sodium channels. Consequently intracellular voltage becomes positive, resting potential is restored by slow potassium ion efflux.

3.20   **Answers: A B D**

Sleep is characterised by four stages:
1. Appearance of low frequency theta waves
2. Low frequency activity broken by sleep spindles which are transient high frequency (12–14 Hz waves lasting 0.5 seconds) and k complexes which are marked positive followed by negative deflections lasting approximately 0.5 seconds
3. Delta waves account for 20–50%
4. Delta waves over 50%

REM sleep is typical of stage 1 sleep with superimposed saw tooth waves. REM sleep accounts for 50% of sleep in the newborn and decreases with age to approximately 20% by middle age. The duration of REM sleep decreases with each successive sleep cycle and occupies approximately one fifth of total sleep. Sleep cycles typically last 90 minutes but depth of each particular cycle decreases as sleep progresses.

3.21   **Answers: A E**

The biosynthesis of catecholamines is as follows:

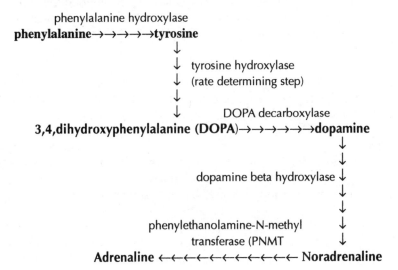

3.22   **Answers: A B D**

Enkephalins are endogenous opioids with a penta-peptide structure derived from the precursor peptide betalipotropin which is in turn derived from Pro-opiomelanocortin (POMC). A number of opioid receptors have been identified including mu (analgesia and craving) and kappa (physical symptoms of opiate withdrawal in combination with noradrenaline in the locus cereolus).

3.23   **Answer: C**

Beta waves are more prominent anteriorly. Lambda waves are present in the occipital region during eye opening and are related to ocular movement.

3.24   **Answer: C**

Schizophrenia has a point prevalence of 3–5 per 100,000. It has equal sex distribution and is associated with left handedness. It accounts for 10–15% of all suicides.

3.25   **Answers: A C E**

Onset is 10–15 years after that of epilepsy. Premorbid personality is normal and it is particularly associated with temporal lobe epilepsy. Non-dominant hemisphere foci is more closely associated with affective psychoses.

3.26   **Answers: C D E**

Indications of a good prognosis in schizophrenia are presence of precipitating factors, acute onset, family history of affective disorder and presence of affective symptoms.

3.27   **Answers: A B E**

Male schizophrenics have on average earlier onset than females by 4–5 years. They are more likely to have structural brain abnormalities and also have a poorer prognosis.

3.28   **Answers: All true**

Initially described by Wernicke and Kleist and more recently by Perris. Thought by some to be akin to bipolar affective disorder.

3.29   **Answers: C D**

There are no gender differences for rates of bi-polar disorder. The life-time prevalence is 0.012%. There is an increased risk of bi-polar disorder in relatives of 7.8% and an increased risk of uni-polar disorder of 11.4%. Typical onset is usually in the mid-twenties but it may occur at any age.

3.30   **Answers: B D**

There is extensive pharmacological evidence supporting the monoaminergic hypothesis as most antidepressants increase monoamine activity. Conversely, reserpine (anti-hypertensive) depletes central monoaminergic neurone stores and causes severe depression. However, there is a delay between the onset of biochemical actions of antidepressants and the clinical therapeutic response of depressed patients of between two to four weeks. Furthermore, not all drugs that enhance monoaminergic pathways have therapeutic antidepressant activity.

3.31   **Answers: B C**

Suicide accounts for 0.7% of deaths per year. Suicide rates are increased in doctors particularly psychiatrists and anaesthetists. It is rare before the age of fourteen but the rate is increasing in adolescence. The rate is also increasing in the elderly where up to 90% of elderly suicides have a depressive illness. Suicide rates in general hospital in-patients are generally low but remain four times higher than in the general population. Those most at risk are patients admitted following deliberate self-harm, patients with chronic debilitating illnesses, patients investigated for physical complaints which are actually part of a depressive illness and women with post-partum psychiatric illness. Rates in prisons are increased by three to four times those of the general population particularly in remand prisoners and those convicted of violent offences.

3.32   **Answer: B**

The only absolute contraindication for ECT is raised intracranial pressure. Relative contraindications include recent myocardial infarction, cardiac arrhythmia, history of cerebrovascular accident (CVA) and pulmonary disease. The risk of treatment must be weighed against the risk of illness.

3.33   **Answers: B C D E**

PTSD is precipitated by events outside the normal human experience; the event is re-experienced as dreams or flashbacks; there is avoidance of triggering stimuli. Other symptoms include survivor guilt, exaggerated startle response, sleep difficulties and phobias. Associated features are depression, irritability, impulsive behaviour and alcohol and drug abuse. A positive personal or family history for psychiatric disease increases risk of developing PTSD.

3.34   **Answers: A C E**

Mania commonly presents with overactivity, distractibility, irritability, elation and hostility. Grandiose ideas and delusions can occur in 80% of episodes; ideas of reference 40%; auditory hallucinations 30–40%; visual hallucinations 10–20%; first rank schizophrenic symptoms 10–15%.

3.35   **Answers: A B D E**

It is (B1) thiamine deficiency that usually initially causes Wernicke's encephalopathy and then Korsakoff's psychosis. Retrograde amnesia extends back over a period of one year or more prior to the onset of the psychosis.

3.36   **Answers: A B D E**

Glue-sniffing is ten times more common in boys than in girls. It is most prevalent amongst teenagers, particularly in urban areas. It leads to rapid intoxication with initial euphoria and later drowsiness and depression. It commonly produces visual illusions and hallucinations and is associated with reckless and aggressive behaviour. Psychological dependence develops rapidly.

3.37   **Answers: A B D**

Memory loss, amnesia, can be divided into organic and psycho-genic causes; organic amnesia is associated with confabulation, reporting of false past events, and déjà vu phenomena, a sense of having experienced the novel situation before, whilst dissociative amnesia is psychogenic memory and identity loss leaving the personality intact. Cotard's syndrome is an example of a nihilistic delusion and extracampine hallucinations are those that are outside of a person's sensory modality.

3.38   **Answers: All true**

There are three important variants of hydrocephalus:

- obstructive and communicating – secondary to brain atrophy
- obstructive and noncommunicating – due to CSF blockage in the ventricles
- normal pressure hydrocephalus, important as a treatable cause of dementia

There is gait disturbance, initial dementia progressing to global involvement of cognitive function and incontinence, appearing early relative to the degree of dementia. There is a history of subarachnoid haemorrhage in 30–35% of cases.

3.39   **Answers: B C D**

Edwards and Gross defined the syndrome as: stereotyped pattern of drinking, prominence of drink seeking behaviour, increased tolerance to alcohol, repeated withdrawal symptoms, relief or avoidance of alcohol via further drinking, subjective awareness of compulsion to drink and reinstatement after abstinence.

3.40   **Answer: D**

Pseudodementia is more likely where there is an acute onset; a previous history of affective disorder, either personal or in the family; unimpaired ability to learn new information and patchy performance on neuropsychological testing; decline in behaviour appropriate to dementia; and good response to antidepressant treatment.

3.41   **Answers: B C D**

Acute onset in an otherwise stable and healthy relationship is a good prognostic factor. Low sex drive is especially difficult to treat.

3.42   **Answer: A**

Conduct disorder is extremely common. It occurs in both boys and girls 3:1 and is distinct from delinquency which is a legal term for any young person who has committed an offence. Delinquency is far more common in boys (10:1). It has a poor prognosis with almost two-thirds continuing to have problems in adult life.

3.43   **Answers: A C E**

Lens dislocation is found in homocystinuria and Marfan's syndrome. Hypertelorism is found in cri-du-chat syndrome.

3.44   **Answers: All true**

Parotid enlargement is more common in bulimia nervosa but does also occur in anorexics. The changes in bowel habit occur due to paucity of food and laxative abuse. Ulcers and malabsorption also occur.

3.45   **Answers: A C D E**

There is no evident cause for the failure to gain weight despite developmental and cognitive delay and a weight less than the third percentile of the expected weight. The infant is apathetic, irritable and lethargic but most striking is the critical and rejecting attitude of mother towards the infant especially as regards feeding. This is set against a background of emotional and social deprivation.

3.46   **Answers: A B C**

Masters and Johnson describe the 5 stages of: desire mediated by personal, social and hormonal actors; excitement with physiological change, failure at this stage results in erectile impotence; plateau stage, where failure may present as inability to maintain erection and vaginismus; orgasm where failure presents as ejaculatory disorders; resolution where problems may occur with priapism.

3.47   **Answers: A C**

The England and Wales 1983 Mental Health Act has 10 parts and 149 sections. Part I considers the application of the act and the definition of mental disorder. Part II considers compulsory admission to hospital and guardianship. Part II also deals with patients in criminal proceedings or those under sentence. The Act does not use the terms mental retardation or mental handicap. Mental illness is not specifically defined.

3.48   **Answers: All true**

Outside the effects of the primary clinical symptoms there are secondary handicaps from the experience of mental disorder such as withdrawal and avoidance. Tertiary disablement includes restricted social networks, stigma, poverty, unemployment and isolation. Sociologists suggest that diagnosing a person as mentally ill results in them being labelled and opens them up for stigmatisation; the coping responses to this are social withdrawal and attempts to feign competence to try to pass as normal.

3.49   **Answers: A B**

Delusions are abnormal beliefs, maintained with conviction, that are not shared and may be occasionally true.

3.50   **Answers: A B D E**

Note that cataplexy, the sudden loss of muscle strength is not a feature of catatonia. Pareidolia is a type of illusion.

MULTIPLE CHOICE QUESTION PAPER 4

50 questions: time allowed 1 hour 30 minutes

4.1   Kelly's personal construct theory

- ☐ A is nomothetic
- ☐ B proposes man as the artist
- ☐ C is based on constructive alternativism
- ☐ D stipulates the use of personal constructs to predict the future
- ☐ E uses a repertory grid to elicit personal constructs

4.2   Jung

- ☐ A developed individual psychology
- ☐ B identified archetypes
- ☐ C proposed organ inferiority
- ☐ D proposed the collective unconscious
- ☐ E first used the term introvert

4.3   In arousal

- ☐ A the response to a stimulus is linear
- ☐ B the Yerkes–Dodson law is U-shaped
- ☐ C performance is maximal with moderate arousal
- ☐ D arousal can be measured using the galvanic skin response
- ☐ E maximal arousal is desirable when sitting examinations

4.4   Concerning aggression

- ☐ A it is an innate response according to the frustration–aggression hypothesis
- ☐ B the weapon effect has been reported
- ☐ C vicarious learning is stressed in social learning theory
- ☐ D observation of television violence has been shown to increase aggression in children
- ☐ E vicarious catharsis is common

4.5 Long-term memory

☐ A has a limited capacity
☐ B encoding is echoic
☐ C accounts for the recency effect
☐ D accounts for the primacy effect
☐ E is susceptible to state dependent learning

4.6 Perceptual set is determined by

☐ A expectation
☐ B past experience
☐ C cultural factors
☐ D motivation
☐ E emotion

4.7 In adolescence

☐ A the absence of turmoil is pathological
☐ B identification with the parents' basic moral principles is the norm
☐ C the peer group is characteristically opposed to parental moral standards
☐ D identity diffusion involves the inability to formulate clear consistent goals and commitments
☐ E identity for closure involves premature acceptance of an ascribed identity

4.8 Over-inclusive thinking

☐ A is a characteristic feature of anorexia nervosa
☐ B occurs in schizophrenia
☐ C was coined by Schneider
☐ D occurs commonly in obsessive-compulsive disorder
☐ E is also known as tangentiality

4.9 **The following are concepts associated with Sigmund Freud:**

☐ A parapraxes
☐ B organ inferiority
☐ C Oedipus complex
☐ D id
☐ E archetypes

4.10 **The following theorists considered physical appearance to be linked with certain personality types:**

☐ A Adler
☐ B Kretschmer
☐ C Eysenck
☐ D Cattell
☐ E Sheldon

4.11 **The following concepts are associated with the correct person:**

☐ A Bleuler: dementia praecox
☐ B Schneider: differentiation of first and second rank symptoms
☐ C Morel: catatonia
☐ D Hecker: hebephrenia
☐ E Kahlbaum: demence precoce

4.12 **The following drugs can act to precipitate mania:**

☐ A amphetamines
☐ B steroids
☐ C isoniazid
☐ D flupenthixol
☐ E calcium channel blockers

4.13   Benzodiazepines

- ☐ A   can be used to treat anxiety in the short-term
- ☐ B   decrease GABA transmission
- ☐ C   cause ataxia as a side-effect
- ☐ D   cause confusion in the elderly
- ☐ E   cause dependence that is less likely with shorter acting agents

4.14   Neurotensin

- ☐ A   is found in high concentrations in the hypothalamus
- ☐ B   elevates body temperature
- ☐ C   stimulates appetite
- ☐ D   reduces locomotor activity
- ☐ E   modulates the release of dopamine

4.15   Appropriate treatments for lithium toxicity include

- ☐ A   intravenous mannitol
- ☐ B   oral sodium chloride
- ☐ C   alkaline diuresis
- ☐ D   withholding of fluids
- ☐ E   peritoneal dialysis

4.16   The following receptors stimulate G-proteins:

- ☐ A D_1 receptors
- ☐ B $5HT_2$ receptors
- ☐ C   GABA-B receptors
- ☐ D   noradrenergic β_1 receptors
- ☐ E D_2 receptors

4.17   With regard to false perceptions

- ☐ A   eidetic imagery is common amongst children
- ☐ B   completion illusions are extinguished by attention
- ☐ C   pareidolia is a false perception of a real external stimulus
- ☐ D   they occur in schizophrenia
- ☐ E   they include somatic hallucinations

4.18   Side-effects of chronic phenytoin use include

- ☐ A   osteomyelitis
- ☐ B   lanugo
- ☐ C   hypertrichosis
- ☐ D   gingival hyperplasia
- ☐ E   macrocytic anaemia

4.19   Following sudden complete section of the spinal cord:

- ☐ A   spinal reflexes are retained
- ☐ B   urinary incontinence is usually permanent
- ☐ C   stretch reflexes recover within two days
- ☐ D   stretch reflexes recover prior to flexor reflexes
- ☐ E   resting membrane potential of spinal motor neurones is increased

4.20   The following are true of the galvanic skin response:

- ☐ A   it is increased in chronic schizophrenia
- ☐ B   it is increased in anxiety
- ☐ C   it can be used as the basis for a reliable lie detector test
- ☐ D   the electrical conductivity of the skin changes with levels of arousal
- ☐ E   it is a sensitive measure of anxiety

4.21   Gamma amino butyric acid (GABA)

☐ A   is synthesised from glutamic acid
☐ B   is the principal inhibitory neurotransmitter in the CNS
☐ C   is metabolised by non-mitochondrial GABA-transaminase
☐ D   is increased in patients with Huntington's chorea
☐ E   benzodiazepines are GABA antagonists

4.22   Concerning pharmacokinetics

☐ A   in first order kinetics the elimination half-life is proportional to the concentration of a drug at a given time
☐ B   in zero order kinetics the rate of elimination remains constant
☐ C   in zero order kinetics the elimination half-life remains constant
☐ D   steady state is achieved within one to two half-lives
☐ E   dosage interval should remain independent of half-life after steady state has been achieved

4.23   In relation to sleep

☐ A   stage one sleep is associated with the presence of low voltage delta activity
☐ B   stage three sleep is characterised by sleep spindles
☐ C   K complexes are pathological
☐ D   sawtooth waves occur in deep sleep
☐ E   stage three sleep is associated with greater than 50% delta wave activity

4.24   Schizophrenia

☐ A   occurs at a slightly younger age in men than in women
☐ B   is associated with prenatal influenza exposure
☐ C   has an incidence of 1%
☐ D   patients have a suicide rate of 10%
☐ E   is common amongst the homeless

4.25   With regard to schizophrenia

☐   A   the risk in the offspring of two schizophrenics is almost 50%
☐   B   10% of heritability is genetic
☐   C   the disease concordance in dizygotic twins is 50%
☐   D   Lidz described the family processes marital skew and schism
☐   E   it is best explained genetically by a single major locus defect

4.26   Bleuler's primary symptoms of schizophrenia include

☐   A   delusional mood
☐   B   delusional perception
☐   C   catatonic symptoms
☐   D   flattening of affect
☐   E   ambivalence

4.27   Ventricular enlargement in schizophrenia is associated with

☐   A   female gender
☐   B   early age of onset
☐   C   poor prognosis
☐   D   poor cognitive performance
☐   E   good pre-morbid adjustment

4.28   Depression

☐   A   is more common in females than in males
☐   B   has a point prevalence of approximately 20%
☐   C   has a life-time prevalence of 2% for major depression
☐   D   is more common in urban compared with rural populations
☐   E   has an earlier peak onset in males compared with females

4.29   The following disorders may cause depression:

☐ A hyperparathyroidism
☐ B Addison's disease
☐ C brucellosis
☐ D cerebrovascular accident
☐ E Parkinson's disease

4.30   The following are more indicative of depressive rather than catatonic stupor:

☐ A urinary incontinence
☐ B negativism
☐ C stereotypic hand movements
☐ D fixed gaze
☐ E failure to respond to painful stimuli

4.31   The following are associated with an increased suicide risk:

☐ A increasing age
☐ B female gender
☐ C being married
☐ D winter
☐ E Jewish religion

4.32   The following are terms used to describe schizophrenic formal thought disorder:

☐ A fusion
☐ B omission
☐ C derailment
☐ D substitution
☐ E drivelling

4.33   Panic attacks

☐ A   seldom last longer than 1 hour
☐ B   occur in 90% of cases of agoraphobia
☐ C   elevate prolactin levels
☐ D   are always preceded by hyperventilation
☐ E   are commonly associated with depression

4.34   Schizophrenia

☐ A   has an incidence of 1%
☐ B   has a lifetime risk of 3%
☐ C   has an earlier age of onset in females
☐ D   is associated with low fertility
☐ E   has a positive association with rheumatoid arthritis

4.35   With regard to cannabis

☐ A   tetrahydrocannabinol is the main active component
☐ B   it increases spermatogenesis
☐ C   it produces marked bradycardia
☐ D   it is associated with gynaecomastia
☐ E   misuse leads to a strong physical dependence

4.36   Recognised features of delirium include

☐ A   distractibility
☐ B   disorientation in time
☐ C   fluctuating course
☐ D   improvement at night
☐ E   depressed mood

4.37   Alzheimer's disease is associated with

☐ A   increased cerebral acetylcholine
☐ B   decreased cerebral noradrenaline
☐ C   decreased cerebral serotonin
☐ D   decreased GABA
☐ E   decreased somatostatin

4.38   The following are features associated with Parkinson's disease:

☐ A   clinical depression occurs in two-thirds of patients
☐ B   40% of patients develop dementia late in the illness
☐ C   1% of over 70-year-olds suffer from Parkinson's disease
☐ D   there is cell loss in the substantia nigra
☐ E   dopamine loss in the striatum is greater than 90%

4.39   Recognised adverse effects of alcohol dependence are

☐ A   alcoholic hallucinosis with clouding of consciousness
☐ B   Korsakoff's syndrome with clouding of consciousness
☐ C   Wernicke's encephalopathy with clouding of consciousness
☐ D   delirium tremens with clouding of consciousness
☐ E   central medullary myelinosis with clouding of consciousness

4.40   Alzheimer's disease is associated with

☐ A   senile plaques and Lewy bodies
☐ B   autosomal dominant inheritance in some cases
☐ C   Down's syndrome
☐ D   neuroleptic use
☐ E   increased aluminium

4.41   **Techniques described by Masters and Johnson for the treatment of sexual dysfunction include**

- ☐ A   treatment by a single therapist
- ☐ B   weekly treatment sessions for one whole year
- ☐ C   stop-start technique
- ☐ D   squeeze technique
- ☐ E   graded stimulation

4.42   **Encopresis**

- ☐ A   is the passage of semi-solid faeces
- ☐ B   is common
- ☐ C   occurs with equal frequency in both boys and girls
- ☐ D   is associated with coercive and obsessional toilet-training
- ☐ E   is described as non-retentive when there is obstruction with eventual overflow

4.43   **In low weight anorexics, plasma levels of the following hormones remain relatively unchanged:**

- ☐ A   T4
- ☐ B   TSH
- ☐ C   prolactin
- ☐ D   growth hormone
- ☐ E   cortisol

4.44   **Haematological features of anorexia nervosa include**

- ☐ A   acanthocytosis
- ☐ B   raised ESR
- ☐ C   leukopenia
- ☐ D   anaemia
- ☐ E   thrombocytopenia

4.45 **Parents responsible for non-accidental injury to their children are most likely to be**

- ☐ A single
- ☐ B unemployed
- ☐ C themselves victims of abuse as children
- ☐ D from ethnic minority background
- ☐ E alcohol dependent

4.46 **The following drugs are recognised to cause impotence in males:**

- ☐ A lithium
- ☐ B thioridazine
- ☐ C ranitidine
- ☐ D bendrofluazide
- ☐ E methyldopa

4.47 **Typical injuries in non-accidental injury to children include**

- ☐ A multiple bruising
- ☐ B burns
- ☐ C subperiosteal bleeding
- ☐ D scaphoid fracture
- ☐ E ruptured abdominal viscera

4.48 **Sources of non-compliance with medication among psychiatric patients in primary care include**

- ☐ A early recovery
- ☐ B fear of addiction
- ☐ C failure of doctors to warn patients and explain about side-effects
- ☐ D frequent monitoring of compliance by GPs
- ☐ E long intervals between consultations

4.49 Adjustment disorder

☐ A onset of symptoms occurs within one month of exposure to stressor
☐ B is also known as culture shock
☐ C in children can lead to thumb-sucking
☐ D lacks depressive symptoms
☐ E lacks anxiety symptoms

4.50 Lithium

☐ A has no antidepressant properties
☐ B is used as an adjunct to antidepressants
☐ C is a mood stabiliser
☐ D is also used as an anticonvulsant
☐ E is a potent antiemetic

MULTIPLE CHOICE QUESTION PAPER 4 – ANSWERS

4.1   **Answers: C D E**

Kelly's personal construct theory is idiographic and proposes man as the scientist.

4.2   **Answers: B D E**

Jung acknowledged the role of evolution in providing a collective 'racial' unconscious, the contents of which are archetypes. Adler developed individual psychology and described feelings of inferiority as being inevitable and motivating an unconscious drive for compensation.

4.3   **Answers: C D**

The Yerkes–Dodson Law is an inverted U-shape, beyond the peak performance deteriorates.

4.4   **Answers: A B C D**

The weapon effect is the increased likelihood of an aggressive response in the presence of a weapon, even if the weapon itself is not used. Vicarious catharsis is rare but pro-social balance can be promoted by television.

4.5   **Answer: E**

Encoding is semantic and iconic. Primacy and recency effects are aspects of short-term memory. State dependent learning occurs with alcohol and benzodiazepines so that retrieval is more efficient if in a state similar to that when learning initially took place.

4.6   **Answers: All true**

Set is a predisposition to perceive particular features of a particular stimulus.

4.7   **Answers: B D E**

Parents and offspring generally have more in common in terms of attributes and values than adolescents and their peer groups.

4.8   **Answer: B**

Over-inclusive thinking is the inability to circumscribe a problem or retain meaningful boundaries. It was described by Cameron and ideas vary from vaguely related to totally irrelevant. It occurs in schizophrenia. In anorexia nervosa the patient entertains over-valued ideas. Tangentiality describes an oblique verbal response that only glances at the gist.

4.9   **Answers: A C D**

Freud conceptualised a conflict between the unconscious (id) and conscious (ego) mind with slips of the tongue (parapraxes) and dreams as signs of this conflict. The Oedipal complex was postulated to be crucial in male development; the child loving the parent of the opposite sex, fearing the same sex parent as a rival and fearing castration as retribution – this resolves through identification with the same sex parent. Archetypes are associated with Jung, and organ inferiority with Adler.

4.10   **Answers: B E**

Both Kretschmer (pyknic, aesthetic and athletic) and Sheldon (endo-, ecto- and mesomorphic) linked different body builds with specific personality traits such as relaxed/sociable, selfconscious/solitary and robust/outgoing, respectively.

4.11   **Answers: B D**

Morel applied the term demence precoce to a condition of intellectual decline in 1852; Hecker described hebephrenia in 1871; Kahlbaum described catatonia in 1874; Kraepelin used the term dementia praecox to include catatonia, hebephrenia and paranoia in 1896; Bleuler introduced the term schizophrenia (splitting of psychic functions) in 1911, and Schneider proposed his first rank symptoms of schizophrenia in 1939.

4.12   **Answers: A B C**

A range of drugs may precipitate mania: amphetamines, steroids, L-dopa, isoniazid and amantadine. Flupenthixol, an antipsychotic has been shown to have some antidepressant effects.

4.13   **Answers: A C D**

Benzodiazepines are thought to have their action on benzodiazepine receptors that enhance GABA function. They are indicated for the short-term treatment of anxiety and insomnia; however they are prone to cause both physical and psychological dependence, greater with the short acting agents, and require judicious prescribing. Other significant side-effects are drowsiness, nausea, ataxia, confusion in the elderly, slight respiratory depression and amnesia when given in larger doses.

4.14   **Answers: A D E**

Neurotensin reduces body temperature, food intake and locomotor activity.

4.15   **Answers: A B C E**

Initially, stop lithium administration and increase fluid intake. Give sodium chloride orally and intravenous mannitol. If the level is in excess of 3 mmol/l carry out peritoneal/haemodialysis and forced alkaline diuresis.

4.16   **Answers: A C D**

G protein inhibitors include D_2–D_4 ; α_2; $5HT_{1a}$, 1_b and 1_d; and opioid mu receptors. $5HT_2$ receptors increase phosphatidyl inositol.

4.17   **Answers: All true**

False perceptions include illusions, eidetic images and hallucinations. There are three types of illusion: completion and affect illusions that are extinguished by attention and pareidolia that may be heightened by attention. Eidetic imagery is the recollection of a memory as an hallucination.

4.18   **Answers: C D E**

Dose-related adverse effects of phenytoin use include sedation, ataxia and dysarthria. Chronic use results in folate deficient anaemia (macrocytic), osteomalacia, cerebellar atrophy, gingival hyperplasia and hypertrichosis. Lanugo is usually a feature of anorexia nervosa.

4.19 **Answers: D E**

Spinal shock usually lasts at least two weeks in humans. All spinal reflexes are depressed. Reflexes return in the following order: stretch – flexor (protective withdrawal response to noxious stimuli) – postural – stepping. Resting membrane potential of motor neurone is 2–6 mV greater than normal.

4.20 **Answers: A B D**

The galvanic skin response is a measure of arousal of which anxiety is only one component. It is based on changes in the electrical conductivity of the skin. It is increased in chronic schizophrenia and it is thought that some negative symptoms may be employed to decrease hyperarousal. It forms the basis of some lie detectors but is an unreliable test.

4.21 **Answers: A B**

GABA is facilitated by benzodiazepines at the GABA-benzo-diazepine-receptor complex and is metabolised by mitochondrial GABA transaminase. Deficiencies may arise due to vitamin B6 deficiency (co-factor for glutamic acid decarboxylase) leading to convulsions.

4.22 **Answers: A B**

Steady state is normally achieved within four to five half-lives.

4.23 **Answers: All false**

Stage one sleep is associated with the appearance of theta waves. Stage two sleep is associated with sleep spindles and K complexes. Stage three sleep is associated with delta waves 20–50%. Stage four sleep is associated with over 50% delta waves. Sawtooth waves occur during REM sleep.

4.24 **Answers: A B D E**

Schizophrenia has an incidence of 15 to 20 per 100,000 per year. Average age of onset in males and females is 28years and 32 years, respectively. Almost half the homeless have schizophrenia.

4.25   **Answers: A D**
About 70% of the heritability of schizophrenia is thought to be genetic. It probably best fits multifactorial models (gene and environment interaction). Disease concordance is 50% in monozygotic twins and only 10% in dizygotic twins.

4.26   **Answers: D E**
Bleuler's primary symptoms of schizophrenia also include loosening of associations. Other symptoms that are considered to be secondary are hallucinations and delusions.

4.27   **Answers: B C D**
Ventricular enlargement in schizophrenia is associated with poor premorbid adjustment and male gender. There is no association with negative symptomatology or family history. However, early age of onset, poor cognitive performance and poor prognosis are associated.

4.28   **Answers: A B D**
Major depression has a life-time prevalence of approximately 6%. Women have a peak onset in their thirties whilst males have a peak onset in their forties. Depressive pseudodementia may also occur, particularly in the elderly. Thinning of the outer third of the eyebrow is a sign of hypothyroidism. A blunted affect is associated with schizophrenia.

4.29   **Answers: All true**
Other organic causes of depression include endocrine disorders, hypothyroidism and Cushing's syndrome. Infective causes include post influenza and hepatitis. Metabolic causes include hypocalcaemia, anaemia (iron, B12 or folate deficiency) and hypomagnesaemia. Neurological causes also include multiple sclerosis, epilepsy and tumours.

4.30   **Answer: D**
All, except fixed gaze, are more common in catatonic stupor.

4.31   **Answer: A**

Suicide is associated with unemployment, divorce, male gender, increasing age, urban populations, spring, low social class (lowest in middle class) and mental illness. Strong religious beliefs are protective. High risk occupations include doctors, lawyers and publicans. There has been a recent increase of suicide in adolescents (particularly young men) and the elderly.

4.32   **Answers: All true**

Formal thought disorder refers to disorders of the process of thinking and the expression of thoughts. Schneider (Carl) described derailment, drivelling, fusion, omission and substitution. These describe the shifting from one thought to another without connection, mixing of parts of a thought, joining separate thoughts in an unclear manner, missing out large parts of a thought and replacing one thought with an unconnected thought, respectively.

4.33   **Answers: A B**

Panic attacks seldom occur in the absence of other anxiety disorders, with a 90% overlap with agoraphobia. The attack usually lasts about 20 minutes, rarely more than an hour. Hyperventilation is a common concomitant. Prolactin levels can be used to confirm seizure activity.

4.34   **Answer: D**

The lifetime risk of schizophrenia is approximately 1%. The incidence is 15 to 20 per 100,000 of the population per year. The usual age of onset is a 15 to 45 years; in males the onset is 5 years earlier. Patients are more often single and show low fertility. There is a negative association with rheumatoid arthritis. Second generation West Indians show an excess of this disorder.

4.35   **Answers: A D**

Cannabis produces mainly a psychological dependence. It diminishes spermatogenesis and usually produces a tachycardia. It is derived from *Cannabis sativa* (hemp plant) in two main forms (marijuana and hashish).

4.36   **Answers: A B C**

Delirium is characterised by impaired attention, distractibility and disorientation in time, place and person (usually developing in that order). The individual is fearful, confused and often experiencing illusions and hallucinations leading to misidentification and bizarre behaviour. The symptoms generally worsen at night.

4.37   **Answers: B C D E**

Alzheimer's disease is associated with cell loss in the nucleus basalis of Meynert (acetylcholine), locus caeruleus (noradrenaline), raphe nuclei (serotonin) and reduced intrinsic neurotransmitters (GABA and somatostatin).

4.38   **Answers: C D E**

Parkinson's disease occurs in 1% of over 70-year-olds, with peak incidence in the sixth decade. It is characterised by a triad of rigidity, akinesia and tremor. Depression occurs in one-third of patients and dementia in 20% of patients later in the illness. There is significant cell loss in the substantia nigra with depletion of striatal dopamine greater than 90%. Lewy bodies are found in the striatum, and in the cortex to a much more variable extent, on neuropathological examination.

4.39   **Answers: C D**

Whilst alcoholic hallucinosis, Korsakoff's syndrome, Wernicke's encephalopathy and delirium tremens are recognised adverse effects of alcohol dependence, only Wernicke's encephalopathy and delirium tremens occur with clouding of consciousness. Other adverse effects are tremulousness, convulsions, ocular palsies, nystagmus, central pontine myelinosis and peripheral neuropathy.

4.40   **Answers: B C E**

Alzheimer's disease is associated with senile plaques and neuro-fibrillary tangles (Lewy bodies are seen in Lewy body dementia and Parkinson's disease). It does occur in an autosomal dominant fashion with variable penetrance in some families. Alzheimer's disease also occurs in Down's syndrome and there is a postulated link with chromosome 21 and amyloid dysregulation. Acetylcholine is reduced and treatments increasing availability have shown moderate success. Aluminium is found in the brains of patients and dialysis causes a dementia due to high aluminium levels.

4.41   **Answers: D E**

For the treatment of sexual dysfunction Masters and Johnson described a two-week residential treatment programme with the involvement of two therapists per couple. They also described graded stimulation for impotence, super stimulation for ejaculatory failure and graded dilatation for vaginismus. The squeeze technique was used to treat premature ejaculation as indeed is the stop-start technique. The latter was described by Kaplan.

4.42   **Answer: D**

Encopresis is the passage of formed faeces in the absence of physical pathology after the age of 4 years. It is uncommon and occurs far more frequently in boys than in girls. It is described as retentive and non-retentive (primary-continuous and secondary-discontinuous). Coercive and obsessional toilet-training may lead to an aggressive and angry reaction in which the child retains the faeces and eventually has overflow. This is described as retentive.

4.43   **Answers: A B C**

Growth hormone and cortisol levels are raised but the others are within normal range. FSH and LH levels tend to be low.

4.44   **Answers: A C D E**

Anaemia and thrombocytopenia occur in approximately one-third of anorexics, leukopenia occurs in up to two-thirds. Severe anorexics can develop pancytopenia and bone marrow hypoplasia. ESR is lowered not raised.

4.45   **Answers: A B C**

Risk factors amongst parents include: social isolation, adverse living conditions and, particularly, ongoing current stresses such as ill-health. They are likely to have unrealistic expectations of the child and use physical punitive measures for discipline and apply these inconsistently.

4.46   **Answers: B D E**

Tricyclic antidepressants, MAOIs and traditional antipsychotics, especially thioridazine are known to cause impotence and delayed ejaculation; hypotensive agents, diuretics, and alcohol cause impotence. Cimetidine, but not ranitidine, is associated with impotence and reduced sexual drive.

4.47   **Answers: A B C E**

Other typical injuries in non-accidental injury to children include lacerations, multiple fractures and subdural haematoma.

4.48   **Answers: A B C E**

Non-compliance is an important cause of relapse in psychiatric patients; whilst this is minimised in the in-patient setting, it requires careful attention in the community. Early recovery, fear of addiction, adverse and unexplained side-effects, lack of frequent monitoring and longer times between consultations result in decreased compliance.

4.49   **Answers: A B C**

Symptoms of anxiety and depression are the main complaints.

4.50   **Answers: B C**

Lithium on its own has a mild antidepressant effect and is commonly used to augment the effects of antidepressants. It is most often used as a mood stabiliser and side-effects include nausea and vomiting.

MULTIPLE CHOICE QUESTION PAPER 5

50 questions: time allowed 1 hour 30 minutes

5.1 The repertory grid

☐ A can be subject to factor analysis
☐ B can be used in schizophrenic patients with thought disorder
☐ C uses elements which must be people
☐ D uses constructs which are never bipolar opposites
☐ E identifies constructs by comparing similarities and differences amongst elements

5.2 Defence mechanisms include

☐ A isolation of affect
☐ B identification with the aggressor
☐ C projective identification
☐ D introjection
☐ E undoing

5.3 The following phenomenological terms are correctly described:

☐ A metonym: a mild form of loss of speech
☐ B malapropism: an imprecise expression approximating to the intended word and meaning
☐ C paralogia: parrot fashion repetition of another individual's speech
☐ D logoclonia: abrupt cessation of speech mid-sentence; a verbal form of clonus
☐ E palalalia: soft utterances with no significant meaning but said in a very friendly tone

5.4   Bystander intervention is more likely

□ A   in the presence of others
□ B   according to the perceived confidence of the bystander
□ C   in the absence of time pressure
□ D   if the victim is bleeding
□ E   if the victim smells of alcohol

5.5   In language development

□ A   Chomsky's phrase structure rules rearrange strings of symbols
□ B   the theory of transformational grammar was proposed by Chomsky
□ C   phrase structure rules only apply to the English language
□ D   kernal sentences appear earlier than non-kernal sentences
□ E   Chomsky proposed the language aquisition device

5.6   Having undergone cataract surgery to restore eyesight adult subjects can

□ A   fixate objects
□ B   identify faces previously familiar by touch
□ C   display perceptual constancy
□ D   distinguish between geometric shapes without resorting to touch or counting corners
□ E   distinguish figure from ground

5.7   In normal ageing

□ A   height decreases due to osteoporosis
□ B   nerve impulses are 5% slower
□ C   longsightedness occurs
□ D   the rate of liver cell regeneration decreases
□ E   sperm production ceases in males

5.8   Concerning auditory hallucinations

☐ A   they are described as elementary when an individual hears
         voices early in the course of an illness
☐ B   Gedankenlautwerden describes an auditory hallucination in
         which the individual's own thoughts are spoken aloud, the
         voice being heard immediately after the thought
☐ C   thought echo is also known as thought sonalisation
☐ D   the term imperative hallucinations is sometimes used to
         describe hallucinations that are critical to diagnosis
☐ E   they are pathognomonic of schizophrenia

**5.9   The following are recognised defence mechanisms in dynamic
         psychopathology:**

☐ A   denial
☐ B   projection
☐ C   rationalisation
☐ D   transition
☐ E   sublimation

**5.10   Personality was described using the following dimensions by
         Eysenck and Cattell:**

☐ A   introversion-extroversion
☐ B   neuroticism-stability
☐ C   psychoticism-stability
☐ D   psychological-physical
☐ E   emotional-reserved

5.11   With regard to visual hallucinations

☐ A   autoscopic hallucinations are common
☐ B   Lilliputian hallucinations are sometimes described as pleasurable
☐ C   experiential hallucinations occur in temporal lobe epilepsy
☐ D   they are common in schizophrenia
☐ E   they are also called phosphenes

5.12   Clozapine

☐   A   is the prototypic atypical antipsychotic drug
☐   B   has greater affinity for the serotonergic receptors than
              dopaminergic receptors
☐   C   does not cause extrapyramidal side-effects even at large doses
☐   D   can cause agranulocytosis in 3% of patients
☐   E   can precipitate seizures within the recommended dose range

5.13   Recognised side-effects of ECT include

☐   A   memory disturbance
☐   B   headache
☐   C   nystagmus
☐   D   vomiting
☐   E   musculoskeletal pains

5.14   Recognised complications of lithium administration include

☐   A   T-wave tenting
☐   B   choreoathetosis
☐   C   tardive dyskinesia
☐   D   nasal congestion
☐   E   ataxia

5.15   In psychopharmacology

☐   A B_{max} measures the density of receptors per unit of tissue
☐   B   Kd measures the affinity of an endogenous transmitter or drug
              binding to a receptor
☐   C   sensitisation occurs on repeated exposure to amphetamines
☐   D   amphetamines can cause kindling
☐   E   glycine increases calcium flux at NMDA receptors

5.16   Negativism

☐   A   is seen in dementia
☐   B   describes the pessimism characteristic of treatment resistant
              depression
☐   C   is associated with severe mental handicap
☐   D   describes the movement of protons during magnetic resonance
☐   E   is the opposite of gegenhalten (opposition)

**5.17   Characteristic features of speech and thought in mania
           include**

☐   A   clang associations
☐   B   logorrhoea
☐   C   alogia
☐   D   prolixity
☐   E   dysphonia

5.18   Hemisection of the spinal cord at T12 causes

☐   A   ipsilateral loss of temperature below the lesion
☐   B   contralateral loss of pain below the lesion
☐   C   ipsilateral motor paralysis above the lesion
☐   D   astereognosis
☐   E   brisk ipsilateral knee jerk

5.19   A complete lesion of the oculomotor nerve will cause

☐   A   ptosis
☐   B   external strabismus
☐   C   diplopia
☐   D   pupillary dilation
☐   E   failure of accommodation

5.20   Dopamine

☐   A   is decreased in the substantia nigra in those with Parkinson's disease
☐   B   stimulates prolactin secretion
☐   C   is a neurotransmitter in the cerebellum
☐   D   is metabolised mainly to dihydroxyphenylacetic acid in humans
☐   E   in lower primates is metabolised mainly to homovanillic acid

5.21   The following are true:

☐   A   polar compounds cross the blood-brain barrier relatively easily
☐   B   the blood-brain barrier is fully developed in neonates
☐   C   in the elderly, the volume of distribution for benzodiazepines is increased
☐   D   breast milk is more acidic than plasma
☐   E   adult GFR is not reached until the age of five years

5.22   REM sleep is associated with

☐   A   increased cerebral blood flow
☐   B   penile erection
☐   C   myoclonic jerks
☐   D   loss of muscle tone
☐   E   decreased protein synthesis in animal experiments

5.23   Pathognomonic symptoms of schizophrenia include

☐   A   running commentary
☐   B   Gedankenlautwerden
☐   C   thought broadcast
☐   D   delusional perception
☐   E   somatic passivity

5.24 **The dopamine theory of schizophrenia is supported by the following:**

☐   A   L-dopa administration can cause positive symptoms of schizophrenia
☐   B   disulfiram exacerbates schizophrenia
☐   C   antipsychotic efficacy correlates with D2 receptor occupancy
☐   D   amphetamine administration can cause positive symptoms of schizophrenia
☐   E   only the D2 receptor antagonist isomer of flupenthixol is an effective antipsychotic

5.25 **Double-bind communication**

☐   A   involves the generation of internal conflict
☐   B   occurs in states of emotional arousal
☐   C   is usually received from a familiar figure
☐   D   was described by Bateson
☐   E   usually involves siblings

5.26 **Structural brain imaging in schizophrenics has shown the following structures to be significantly smaller:**

☐   A   hippocampus
☐   B   amygdala
☐   C   caudate
☐   D   ventricles
☐   E   putamen

5.27 **In severe depression the following signs occur:**

☐   A   decreased rate of blinking
☐   B   thinning of the outer third of the eyebrow
☐   C   persecutory delusions
☐   D   auditory hallucinations
☐   E   blunted affect

5.28   The following drugs may cause depression:

☐   A   methyldopa
☐   B   flupenthixol
☐   C   clonidine
☐   D   frusemide
☐   E   digoxin

5.29   The following are diagnostic observer rated scales for depression:

☐   A   Beck Depression Inventory
☐   B   Montgomery–Asberg Scale
☐   C   Hamilton Depression Scale
☐   D   Zung Depression Scale
☐   E   Wakefield Scale

5.30   Concerning suicide

☐   A   the majority of suicides suffer from depression
☐   B   the risk is significantly increased in schizophrenia with high pre-morbid educational achievement
☐   C   co-morbid obsessive-compulsive disorder in depressed patients increases risk
☐   D   rheumatoid arthritis increases risk
☐   E   high cholesterol levels have been reported to increase risk

5.31   Generalised anxiety disorder is associated with

☐   A   derealisation
☐   B   marked autonomic symptoms such as palpitations
☐   C   depression
☐   D   increased genetic concordance in close relatives
☐   E   a prevalence of 2–5% of the population

5.32 **Evidence supporting a difference between unipolar and bipolar affective disorder shows**

- ☐ A different average age of onset
- ☐ B genetic evidence
- ☐ C differential treatment response to lithium prophylaxis
- ☐ D differential response to tricyclic antidepressant treatment
- ☐ E different symptomatology

5.33 **Genetic risk in schizophrenia is as follows:**

- ☐ A a small difference in concordance between monozygotic and dizygotic twins
- ☐ B the risk in first degree relatives of schizophrenics is around 10%
- ☐ C the child with both parents suffering from schizophrenia carries a 40–50% risk
- ☐ D the mode of inheritance is likely to be a single dominant gene
- ☐ E adoption studies suggest the risk of schizophrenia is related to the adopted parents' genetic risk

5.34 **Recognised sequelae of heroin use include**

- ☐ A endocarditis
- ☐ B cardiomyopathy
- ☐ C tuberculosis
- ☐ D nephrotic syndrome
- ☐ E hepatitis

5.35 **Recognised features of dementia include**

- ☐ A perseveration
- ☐ B clouding of consciousness
- ☐ C initial amnesia for remote events
- ☐ D catastrophic reactions
- ☐ E personality deterioration

5.36   **The following illnesses commonly result in damage to the frontal and temporal cortex:**

☐ A   Jakob-Creutzfeldt disease
☐ B   herpes encephalitis
☐ C   tertiary syphilis
☐ D   Binswanger's disease
☐ E   carbon monoxide poisoning

5.37   **Wilson's disease**

☐ A   is a rare cause of psychosis
☐ B   is associated with increased serum copper
☐ C   is associated with Kaiser-Fleischer rings on the finger nails
☐ D   usually has an onset in the third decade
☐ E   is an autosomal dominant condition

5.38   **The following drugs and their recognised associations are correctly paired:**

☐ A   heroin: miosis, hypotension and respiratory depression
☐ B   amphetamines: schizophreniform psychosis with chronic use
☐ C   cocaine: serotonin re-uptake inhibition with hallucinations and formication
☐ D   cannabis: anticholinergic effects and acute toxic psychosis
☐ E   LSD: serotonin re-uptake inhibition and visual hallucinations

5.39   **Masters and Johnson's phases of sexual response include**

☐ A   plateau
☐ B   excitement
☐ C   stimulation preparedness
☐ D   resolution
☐ E   relief

5.40 The following are recognised treatments for hyperactivity in children:

- ☐ A imipramine
- ☐ B clonidine
- ☐ C dexamphetamine
- ☐ D pemoline
- ☐ E methylphenidate

5.41 The following are recognised features of anorexia nervosa:

- ☐ A anaemia
- ☐ B hypocholesterolaemia
- ☐ C hypothalamic hypogonadism
- ☐ D tachycardia
- ☐ E bradycardia

5.42 Periodic episodes of repetitive and stereotyped limb movements occur in

- ☐ A uraemia
- ☐ B first month of pregnancy
- ☐ C Pickwickian syndrome
- ☐ D narcolepsy
- ☐ E benzodiazepine withdrawal

5.43 Features of children that are associated with child abuse include

- ☐ A low birth weight
- ☐ B physically unattractive
- ☐ C product of unwanted pregnancy
- ☐ D being breast-fed
- ☐ E neonatal maternal separation

5.44   Anorexia nervosa is defined by

☐   A   weight loss greater than 15 kg
☐   B   fear of fatness
☐   C   amenorrhoea in women
☐   D   erectile failure in men
☐   E   loss of appetite

5.45   Characteristic features of Piblokto include

☐   A   occurrence mainly in Mediterranean countries
☐   B   occurrence predominantly in men
☐   C   extreme elation
☐   D   usually following an alcoholic binge
☐   E   vividly remembered and easily described episodes

5.46   The following statements are true:

☐   A   gender dysphoria is associated with Klinefelter's syndrome
☐   B   transsexualism is more common in females than in males
☐   C   transvestism is a form of fetish
☐   D   gender dysphoric disorder is associated with homosexuality
☐   E   impotence can be effectively treated using tricyclic antidepressants

5.47   Concerning puerperal disorders

☐   A   post-traumatic stress disorder (PTSD) is common following childbirth
☐   B   post-partum psychosis affects 1 in 10 mothers
☐   C   they can lead to filicide
☐   D   post-partum psychosis usually begins 1–2 weeks after childbirth
☐   E   querulent reactions occur in about 50% of new mothers

5.48   **The following statements about antidepressants are correct:**

☐ A   the most common adverse effect of fluoxetine is nausea
☐ B   mianserin is an alpha-2 adrenoceptor antagonist
☐ C   venlafaxine has a wide dose range
☐ D   clomipramine inhibits the re-uptake of both noradrenaline and serotonin
☐ E   mirtazapine is a reversible monoamine oxidase inhibitor

5.49   **Psychodynamic interpersonal therapy**

☐ A   was developed by Hobson
☐ B   involves mainly the use of questions
☐ C   is as effective as CBT in the treatment of depression
☐ D   involves focusing on negative cognitions
☐ E   is ineffective in the treatment of irritable bowel syndrome

5.50   **The International Classification of Diseases and Health Related Problems tenth revision 1992 (ICD-10)**

☐ A   does not describe the term neurasthenia
☐ B   categorises disorders along five axes
☐ C   cannot be used for research diagnoses
☐ D   includes schizoaffective disorders under disorders of mood (affective disorders, F30–F39)
☐ E   places post-schizophrenic depression under disorders of mood (affective disorders, F30–F39)

MULTIPLE CHOICE QUESTION PAPER 5 – ANSWERS

5.1   **Answers: A B E**
Constructs are always bipolar opposites and elements may take any form.

5.2   **Answers: All true**
Isolation of affect: the separation of an idea from its attached original affect.
Identification: the unconscious adoption of desirable attributes of others, which enhance self-esteem through affiliation.
Introjection: the transposition of external objects and their qualities into the self; the symbolic assimilation and internalisation of an object.
Undoing: the negation of a prior unacceptable behaviour.

5.3   **Answers: All false**
A metonym is an imprecise expression that approximates to the intended word. Malapropism is the ludicrous misuse of words. Paralogia is the verbal expression of positive thought disorder. Palalalia is the repetition of a word, usually the last in a phrase or sentence with increasing frequency. Logoclonia is a form of perseveration involving the repetition of the last syllable of the last word.

5.4   **Answers: B C**
Bystander intervention in the presence of others is unlikely because of pluralistic ignorance and diffusion of responsibility. If the victim is bleeding the bystander is more likely to get someone else to help, particularly if there is low perceived confidence.

5.5   **Answers: B D E**
Phrase structure rules replace single symbols with different sets of symbols and can generate sentences in any language when applied systematically. In kernal sentences, phrase structures do not undergo transformations.

5.6   **Answers: A E**
Following restoration of eyesight simple figural unity is immediately available being independent of previous visual experience, but complex figural identity requires prolonged training.

5.7   **Answers: C D**

The height decrease is related to connective tissue changes in the vertebral column. Nerve impulses are up to 20% slower. Sperm production continues until death in most males.

5.8   **Answer: C**

Elementary hallucinations are basic sounds such as noises or whistles. Gedankenlautwerden describes the synchronous occurrence of voices and thoughts. In 'echo de la pensées' the voice is heard immediately after the thought. Imperative hallucinations are command hallucination. Auditory hallucinations occur in many disorders (e.g. severe depression, organic illnesses) and not solely in schizophrenia.

5.9   **Answers: A B C E**

Defence mechanisms used to cope with unconscious:conscious mind conflicts were suggested to be: reaction formation, acceptance of opposite ideal; denial; rationalisation, basic urges given a more acceptable explanation; sublimation, urge changes into praiseworthy actions; projection, feelings attributed to another; displacement, hostile feelings transferred towards another; and regression to an earlier developmental stage.

5.10   **Answers: A B C**

Eysenck and Cattell described personality using continuous dimensions or traits inferred from behaviour. The Eysenck personality questionnaire describes personality as behaviour in the three dimensions of intraversion-extraversion, neuroticism-stability and psychoticism-stability.

5.11   **Answer: B C**

Visual hallucinations occur more often in organic disorders than in schizophrenia. Phosphenes are flashes of light that are perceived upon direct stimulation of the occipital cortex. Visual hallucinations of oneself (autoscopic hallucinations; Doppelgänger) are relatively rare.

5.12   **Answers: A B C E**

Clozapine is the prototypic atypical antipsychotic with an absence of propensity to cause extrapyramidal side-effects even at higher doses. It requires regular haematological monitoring as it causes agranulocytosis in approximately 0.8% of patients. Its main action is thought to be on the serotonergic system as its affinity for this is higher than for dopamine receptors. It can cause seizures and, at higher doses, concomitant use of antiepileptic agents is suggested.

5.13   **Answers: A B E**

Most of these side-effects of ECT are relatively common but short-lived.

5.14   **Answers: B C D E**

On ECG one may observe T-wave flattening. Adverse effects of lithium also include: fatigue, thirst, tremor of hands, oedema and weight gain.

5.15   **Answers: All true**

The lower the Kd the better the binding. Sensitisation and kindling refer to the repeated application of a drug causing increased activity rather than tolerance or desensitisation.

5.16   **Answers: A C**

Negativism is the accentuated opposition to movements. The resistance is without motive and in milder form it is termed opposition (gegenhalten). It is seen in catatonia, dementia and severe mental handicap. Resonance is the term used to describe the movement of protons to a higher energy level in response to a radio-frequency impulse.

5.17   **Answers: A B D**

Association between words on the basis of similar sound (clang association), voluble pressure of speech (logorrhoea), often reflecting flight of ideas and thought (prolixity) are features of mania. Alogia, a poverty of speech, and dysphonia, an impaired ability to vocalise, are not characteristic of mania.

5.18   **Answers: B E**

Brown-Séquard syndrome (hemisection of the cord) is rare. It is characterised by contralateral loss of temperature and pain below the lesion, ipsilateral loss of proprioception below the lesion and ipsilateral upper motor neurone spastic paralysis causing brisk knee jerks.

5.19   **Answers: All true**

The oculomotor nerve supplies all extraocular muscles except superior oblique (trochlear nerve) and lateral rectus (abducent nerve). It also supplies striated levator palpebrae superioris and the smooth muscles sphincter pupilli, Mueller's muscle and the ciliary muscles.

5.20   **Answer: A**

Dopamine is metabolised to homovanillic acid (HVA) as the major metabolite and dihydroxyphenylacetic acid (DOPAC) the minor metabolite in humans. HVA and DOPAC can be measured in CSF as indices of central dopamine turnover. The important dopaminergic systems are:

A • **Mesolimbic system**
      Ventral tegmental area (VTA)   →   limbic system

B • **Mesocortical system**
      Ventral tegmental area (VTA)   →   frontal cortex and
                                          septohippocampal
                                          region

C • **Tuberoinfundibular system**
      Hypothalamic arcuate nucleus →   median eminence

D • **Nigrostriatal system**
      Substantia nigra pars compacta →   striatum

5.21   **Answers: C D**

Non-polar lipid soluble compounds cross the blood–brain barrier relatively easily compared with polar compounds. In the elderly there is a decrease in total body water and muscle mass with an increase in adipose tissue. Thus the volume of distribution of lipid soluble drugs increases. Adult GFR is achieved at approximately three to five months of age.

5.22   **Answers: A B C D**

Protein synthesis has been reported to be increased during REM sleep in animal studies.

5.23   **Answers: All false**

All of these symptoms are first rank symptoms but none are pathognomonic or exclusively diagnostic as almost a fifth of schizophrenics lack these symptoms and they also occur in those without schizophrenia.

5.24   **Answers: All true**

The dopamine hypothesis proposes excessive mesolibic-cortical dopamine activity.

5.25   **Answers: A B C D**

The social context of the situation in which the conflict arises does not allow escape and so the conflict is sustained. The development of schizophrenia is viewed as a means of coping with this conflict.

5.26   **Answers: A B**

Other parts of the brain that have been shown to be smaller include the parahippocampal gyrus and globus pallidus. The nucleus accumbens, caudate nucleus and putamen are not significantly smaller.

5.27   **Answers: A C D**

Typically the corners of the mouth are turned downwards and there is a vertical furrowing of the central brow. A hunched posture staring at the floor is usually adopted. There is evidence of slowness of thought and movement (psychomotor retardation). Thought content is predominantly pessimistic and may involve thoughts of suicide.

5.28   **Answers: A C E**

Other drugs causing depression include propranolol, reserpine, bromocriptine, phenothiazines and cimetidine.

5.29   **Answers: B C**

The Beck Depression Inventory is not a diagnostic scale but provides an indication of the depth of a depressive illness. The Zung and Wakefield scales are self-rated scales.

5.30   **Answers: A B D**

Over 50 % of completers suffer from depression. Of these, 50% have psychomotor retardation. Thus, this cannot be considered to be protective. In addition to sociodemographic variables risk is increased with insomnia, self-neglect, delusions, hopelessness and previous history of suicide attempt. 20% of completers suffer from alcoholism, 5% of completers suffer from schizophrenia, particularly young males with chronic illness who have recently been discharged, are in remission and have good insight. Personality disorder accounts for 30–40% of particularly anti-social and borderline types (overlaps with other groups). Chronic physical illness increases the risk. Low cholesterol levels have been reported to increase risk although this remains controversial. Depressed patients with co-morbid obsessive-compulsive disorder (OCD) have six-fold lower risk than depressed patients without co-morbid OCD.

5.31   **Answers: All true**

Generalised anxiety disorder is diagnosed when the normal symptoms of anxiety are continuous and unpleasant, cannot be overcome and are out of proportion to the situation. It can be associated with autonomic symptoms; depersonalisation and derealisation can occur and depression commonly coexists. It has increased prevalence in the families of the probands, and point prevalence in the population is 2–5%.

5.32   **Answers: A B D**

Manic-depressive illnesses may be divided into those with depression (unipolar) and those in which both episodes of mania and depression occur (bipolar). In the acute depressive episode there is no difference in symptoms. Bipolar illness has its onset at 25–29 years while unipolar begins at 40–45 years. First degree relatives of bipolars are more likely to be effectively ill than those of unipolars; although lithium is effective in the prophylaxis of both, tricyclics are effective only in unipolars.

5.33   **Answers: B C**

The risk in first degree relatives of schizophrenics is around 10%, the risk for second degree relatives is 3–4%; the child with two schizophrenic parents carries a 40–50% risk. Adoption studies show that the children of schizophrenic mothers are more likely to develop the disorder: 5 out of 47 cases against 0 out of 50 controls in one study. The mode of inheritance is likely to be multi-factorial and polygenic.

5.34   **Answers: A C D E**

The physical complications of heroin use include endocarditis, nephrotic syndrome, tuberculosis, gangrene, hepatitis, thrombophlebitis and HIV infection. Heroin use also carries a risk of injury, poisoning, overdose and emboli. In addition, there are very many social costs of heroin use, particularly because of its expense.

5.35   **Answers: A D E**

Dementia is the impairment of intellectual function in clear consciousness. It is often associated with personality deterioration and memory loss, initially recent and later remote. A catastrophic reaction is the sudden, marked emotional reaction to frustration.

5.36   **Answers: B C**

Herpes encephalitis and syphilis result in frontotemporal damage and atrophy while Jakob-Creutzfeldt disease and carbon monoxide poisoning involve the whole cortex, with basal ganglia, thalamus and hippocampal involvement.

5.37   **Answer: A**

Wilson's disease is an autosomal recessive condition. Onset is usually in the first two decades of life but may be delayed until as late as the fifth. The usual presentation is with liver or CNS involvement; affective and psychotic psychoses have been reported. Investigations reveal serum copper and ceruloplasmin are reduced and 24-hour urinary copper excretion is increased. Kayser-Fleischer rings may be seen on ophthalmic examination. Treatment is with penicillamine.

5.38   **Answers: A B D**

Heroin acts on opiate receptors to produce analgesia, miosis, hypotension, bradycardia and respiratory depression. Amphetamines have a dopamine like effect with chronic use resulting in a schizophreniform psychosis. Cocaine inhibits dopamine re-uptake; excessive use causes a psychosis with paranoia, and hallucinations. Cannabis has anticholinergic effects and can cause an acute toxic psychosis, exacerbating schizophrenia with chronic use. LSD is a serotonin antagonist; inducing visual perceptual changes (hallucinations). Excessive use of LSD can precipitate a schizophreniform psychosis.

5.39   **Answers: A B D**

Four phases were described: excitement, plateau, orgasm and resolution.

5.40   **Answers: All true**

General advice to parents, support and behavioural treatments are useful. Also, in addition to medication, many advocate the use of specific diets although this remains controversial.

5.41   **Answers: A C D E**

Hypercholesterolaemia is a characteristic feature. Hypothalamic hypogonadism occurs because of low serum oestrogen secondary to reduced levels of gonadotrophins. Bradycardia is the usual finding however, tachycardia occurs because of electrolyte imbalance secondary to vomiting and purging.

5.42   **Answers: A C D E**

Described as periodic limb movement disorder. Occurs in almost one-third of those over the age of 60 years. Relatively common cause of insomnia that leads to disrupted sleep and daytime fatigue. Occurs usually in latter half of pregnancy and is aggravated by tricyclics, phenothiazines and monoamine oxidase inhibitors.

5.43   **Answers: A B C E**

These factors are vulnerability factors and others include: habitual restlessness, poor sleep pattern and incessant crying. Mental or physical handicap is also associated with an increased likelihood of physical abuse.

5.44   **Answers: B C**

The core features of anorexia are behaviour intended to cause weightloss (15% below expected or BMI less than 17.5); morbid fear of fatness; and endocrine disturbance. Also amenorrhoea in women and loss of libido in men.

5.45   **Answers: All false**

Piblokto occurs in Eskimo women, typically at times of food shortage. It is associated with symptoms of depression and involves running and jumping into water in a dissociated state. The episode is surrounded by amnesia.

5.46   **Answer: A**

Transsexualism and transvestism are both gender identity disorders. Transsexualism is more common in males than in females. In transvestism the individual experiences a state of appropriateness by wearing clothes of the opposite gender. Sexual dysfunction, including impotence, is often a side-effect of antidepressant therapy.

5.47   **Answers: C D**

Post-partum psychosis occurs in about 0.2% of mothers. The likelihood of recurrence is much greater. It characteristically begins soon after childbirth and untreated can last in excess of 6–8 months. It is more common in primipara and there is often a family history of psychiatric illness. Querulent reactions are relatively uncommon (occurring in about 1% of mothers).

5.48 **Answers: A B C D**

Mirtazapine enhances both noradrenergic and serotonergic neurotransmission. It stimulates alpha-1 adrenoceptors on cell bodies of serotonergic neurones and inhibits alpha-2 adrenoceptors on serotonergic nerve terminals. It also blocks several post-synaptic receptors including 5HT2 and 5HT3 receptors.

5.49 **Answers: A C**

Psychodynamic interpersonal therapy was developed by RF Hobson and can be regarded in its approach as being between that of interpersonal therapy and traditional dynamic psychotherapy. It uses an exploratory rational approach involving staying with feelings and attaining a shared understanding. It has been shown to be effective in depression and irritable bowel syndrome.

5.50 **Answers: All false**

Neurasthenia is categorised under neurotic disorders (F48.0). Schizoaffective disorders and post-schizophrenic depression are both included under schizophrenia, schizotypal and delusional disorders (F20–29). ICD-10 can be used for both clinical and research purposes.

INDEX

Numbers given refer to the relevant question number. The word shown may not always be used in the question, but may appear in the explanatory answer.

Index

RECOMMENDED READING LIST

Companion to Psychiatric Studies, Johnstone, Freeman and Zeally, 6th edition, 1998 Churchill Livingstone.

Examination Notes in Psychiatry; Basic Sciences, a postgraduate text, Malhi and Mitchell, 1st edition, 1999 Butterworth-Heinemann.

Introduction to Psychology, Atkinson, Atkinson, Smith and Ben, 11th edition, 1993 Harcourt Brace.

Symptoms in the mind, Sims, 2nd edition, 1995 Saunders.